D0119533

101

MAKING LOCAL SURVEYS

MAKING LOCAL SURVEYS

AN EYE FOR COUNTRY

BY

CHARLOTTE A. SIMPSON, B.Sc. (Oxon.)

Author of "Rediscovering England" and "The Study of Local Geography"
Collaborator in "The World of Man," Vol. I
and in the Ministry of Education pamphlet
"Village Survey Making"

3/1.36

LONDON
SIR ISAAC PITMAN & SONS, LTD.
PITMAN HOUSE, PARKER ST., KINGSWAY, W.C.2
BATH   MELBOURNE   JOHANNESBURG

First published 1951

No. 89981

Class No. 371.36

PREFACE

FOR many years, students reading Geography at Universities and Training Colleges have been required to show evidence of first-hand observation or research in special districts of their own choice. Even before the war, enterprising teachers in various types of school conducted (often under great difficulty) surveys of the immediate district, with pupils of different ages and attainments. This has been done in order to encourage habits of first-hand study and independent effort, and to arouse interest in the surrounding scenery and natural conditions, and in the past history and present activities of the local people.

Recently, this method of approach to geography, nature study, local history, and study of citizenship has been given more official encouragement. Opportunities to show local knowledge are often given in the papers of public examinations, and competitions in studies of the locality are arranged for Young Farmers' Clubs, Women's Institutes and other bodies. Map-reading, in connexion with geography, has been taught in schools for many years and is an indispensable part of local survey work. Much can be done, too, by reading, and by the use of statistics and other official records. Some teachers and students, however, seem to find difficulty in developing an *eye for country* and in this aspect of the work, which should be its foundation, newcomers to a district are, of course, much handicapped.

An attempt is made in this book to meet the difficulty, and to suggest to teachers, lecturers, or anyone undertaking a local survey, how the approach may best be made. It is hoped that some experience of first-hand observation, out of doors, whether in town or country, will lead to much useful work in schools and colleges (especially, perhaps, the upper forms of Secondary Schools of various types) and also that it may give rise to new

v

hobbies hitherto untried, and to increasing interest and pleasure in travel in this country and abroad.

The Author wishes to acknowledge help from much useful discussion with teachers and students who have done experimental work with her on the Local Survey method, and also to thank Mr. R. Abbott for the loan of the photograph in Plate IX, and the author and publishers of *The School Looks Around* for the use of the diagrams in Map 4.

C. A. S.

CONTENTS

ILLUSTRATIONS

PLATES

MAPS

viii

CHAPTER I

WHY MAKE A LOCAL SURVEY?

IT is a platitude to say that we live in a time of stupendous changes, but perhaps these changes are more impressive to the older people who knew the comparatively placid years before 1914 than to those who have grown up in "modern times" and so cannot fully realize the contrasts between the apparent stability of the late nineteenth century and the more exciting and disturbing years of the twentieth. It is surely important that young people should be encouraged to note and try to understand these changes and what they involve. It is true that young people do, to some extent, realize that the scientific discoveries of former years are being put to greater and more widespread use while fresh discoveries of outstanding importance are being made. They can see that events and ideas are moving more and more rapidly (gathering momentum as it were) and that conditions of life are completely changed since the time of their grandparents and, to some extent, since the time of their parents. But just because these changes are more revolutionary and rapid in development than any since pre-historic times, it is impossible for young people to grasp without special study what the world—even their own neighbourhood—was like only fifty years ago.

The past cannot be entirely swept away, however, and the problems of the present cannot be understood without its influence being taken into account. Moreover the destruction which, during the late war, took from us so much that was useful, beautiful, and instructive, has increased the value of what is left, and whilst we all hope for schemes for a better world we might do well first to gain a general idea of the background for such schemes in order to be able to discriminate between what is of value and should be preserved and what is harmful, useless or ugly and should be replaced by something better.

Perhaps the best way to understand such developments is to watch the changes taking place around us, note the

I

background, and record what is happening before our eyes—in short, to make what is known as a "local survey" in our immediate surroundings. This can be done in different ways.

It is possible to learn a good deal about our local district from books. Local history can be studied, though incompletely, in this way. Certain facts about the physical features of the country, its geology and some of the main uses of the land, can be learned from maps. Economic questions, such as markets, increase and distribution of population, public services, can be worked out from statistics and inquiries from other people. These "second-hand" methods of study are probably needed, sooner or later, to amplify what has been seen at first-hand, and perhaps are specially needed in any urban area, but in the opinion of the writer the best method of approach to the study of any district is by *first-hand observation*, founded on visual impressions, and it is the aim of this book to suggest how this can be carried out. It should be stated here that this method of approach is, on the whole, more suited to rural than to urban districts, though can be applied anywhere (even in surroundings such as the scene in Plate VIII). This book will, however, chiefly stress the advantages of local surveys by schools and study groups in rural districts, where the hobbies and interests to which they give rise are most needed. It will be found that personal observation, if accurate, is more valuable as a training and in the making of records than blind reliance on the opinions of others, however eloquently expressed, and such a training should enable young people to make a careful study of their setting before they decide what new developments they wish to see. One of the objects of the local study to be here described is to help those young enough to take a hand in the shaping of a new world to use their powers of observation and discrimination.

But although this is an adequate reason for the detailed study of a district, it is not the only one. Children are naturally observant, but this faculty is often lost as they grow older and become preoccupied with indoor work. But as the power of observation and of "putting two and two together" is developed, many new hobbies and interests arise. Nowadays more seems to be thought and said about increased hours of leisure than about how this leisure is to be spent, so surely means of passing those free hours happily and profitably will be more and more welcome. Now the joy of local survey work is that the beginner has no idea where it will lead him, or in what he will become interested or skilled as time goes on, or what talents or hobbies that he already has will help him in his work. Scientific accuracy, imagination, enterprise, love of beauty, interest in plants, animals or stones, in architecture or history, or in modern industrial problems, skill in drawing or photography, pleasure in walking or cycling, any or all of these find places in a co-operative effort. The habit of mind thus encouraged is also of value when applied to everyday matters, such as giving clear and accurate information (which is not merely hearsay or guessing) to strangers visiting the district. The habit of accuracy in observation and description is of importance throughout school life, and should be expected from scholars of all ages. And then there is the satisfaction felt by many in the idea of collecting records which might be of value even to naturalists or historians outside the school. There should be, too, a sound training in the use of books for reference, to explain and supplement what has already been seen.

There is another aspect of a local survey which may or may not be thought good: it is never finished! There is infinite scope for individual work as fresh developments in the district can be noted and recorded, and students can often improve on the work of their predecessors, or bring in a fresh point of view or a new method of making it clear. Local inquiries, if tactfully made, can bring teachers and students into touch with people they might not otherwise meet, people who may bring fresh interests into their lives. In this book the term "student" is applied to those who "study," of any age. When a teacher or student has begun to think of embarking on a local survey, some perplexity may be felt as to *how to begin*. Methods of approach vary with the age of the students, the special interests and experience of the teachers, and most of all with the character of the district in which the work is to be done. No two districts present quite the same problems, and no two teachers work in exactly the same way, so there is unlimited scope for individual effort and enterprise.

In the opinion of the writer, a survey for a school should be so planned that pupils of different grades and abilities can take part in it, so that the work can advance from one stage to another. In the higher grades, observations made by younger "surveyors" can be arranged and used. In the elementary stages little can be done beyond the collecting and recording of rather disconnected observations, though even this can be done in an orderly manner. For all ages there should be an encouragement of a love of the countryside and a personal interest in the home town, village, or farm and its activities, together with some instruction in map-reading for future use. Occasional meetings between one group of "surveyors" and another would show that each piece of work is part of a larger whole, and even young children could realize that their beginnings lead to something more important and are not ends in themselves, but help those in higher grades to make a more comprehensive study.

In every stage of the work, the method of approach must depend on the locality. The region (large or small) must be considered *as it is* and *as it was*, not primarily as a school "subject" except, possibly, geography in its widest sense. Geology, history, agriculture, architecture, social conditions—any of these may seem to be of the greatest importance, and one of them may seem to be the obvious beginning, but it will probably be found that some knowledge of the rest will be needed in course of time. Any "projects" undertaken, therefore, must be part of a larger whole.

Although some of the suggested exercises at the end of each chapter in this book are marked as being suitable for younger pupils, no attempt is made to indicate the ages at which these or the other exercises should be worked. The undertakings are so varied and appeal so differently to different individuals that the teacher must decide, after studying the district, how the work should be distributed.

It may be said that the particular district near the school is too dull or too difficult for a satisfactory survey. It is true that some districts lend themselves to this work more obviously than others do, but once a beginning is made, even very simply, in *any* district, all sorts of problems arise and attempts to solve these problems lead on to others, often of intense interest. A practical beginning must be made before the scope of the work is fully realized. We will assume that a teacher who is new to the locality or has not previously studied it in detail wishes to organize a local survey. The first aim must be to cultivate the outlook of an explorer. It has been said that the teacher should be content to explore *with* the pupils. This will certainly happen as time goes on and is all to the good, but is scarcely enough. The teacher should get acquainted with the district first in order to suggest points of major importance to the pupils (although not doing their work for them) and so preventing a waste of time. The obvious way for a teacher to start, therefore, is to take a general look at the district and determine what are the most striking and characteristic features in it. In this book are photographs of certain landscapes which are very different. It is suggested that these should be studied in detail, and the features in them may be compared with certain features in the landscape which is to be studied in the proposed "local survey." The photographs do not all show spectacular scenery, in fact some are taken in the kind of uninspiring surroundings in which many schools have to work, and it may seem that present-day developments destroy much opportunity of noting the natural features of a district. But the transitions from a rural to an urban background are worth watching, and the relative advantages and disadvantages of these changes can be compared. Moreover these very changes sometimes lead to unexpected discoveries—geological formations can be studied in the foundations of new houses or cuttings for roads, and, in many areas unhappily laid waste by enemy action, relics of the early inhabitants of the district have been found. Newly ploughed fields may also bring to light such finds.

On the assumption, then, that the making of a local survey is considered worth while, the following chapters will try to answer the question so often asked—"How do you begin?"

There are two main methods. If time for the study of a locality is limited, such as to that of a short holiday, it is worth while to study local maps and to read all that can be found about the district before you actually see it, and check what you have read by your observations on the spot. This will of course save time, for instance on a tour abroad. But in the case of a school survey during a longer period a surer foundation is laid and your impressions are more independent if you look carefully at the district first, feel that it is a real place where people live and work, and supplement what you see, when necessary, by study "on paper."

The first stage in the work is the careful choice of your area and its boundaries. There is not always an alternative choice within easy reach of a school, and in that case the leader of the group may have a difficult, though rarely an impossible, task. Often there is a choice. It is good if a district near the school has features which at once arouse interest or curiosity and indicate where studies should begin. Much depends on the distance and accessibility from the school of such points of interest and on possibilities of movement within the district, and it is rash to tackle too large an area. Many problems that students would like to work on are ruled out by the fact that the area cannot be visited often enough.

In either rural or urban districts a small area to be studied in detail should, however, be considered as part of a larger whole without which its features could not be understood (see Plate I, Maps 1 and 2). The boundaries of the smaller area can be determined in different ways and for different reasons, but are always important and should be planned carefully.

Either natural features or artificial boundaries may determine the survey area but these should be definite. Part of a river-basin or of a valley, such as a cross-section of a chosen reach of the valley in Plate II, with water-partings as boundaries might be suitable. A group of hills, a small island or peninsula, or a length of coast with the sea as one boundary and distinctive inland features, as in Map 5, might be chosen as a unit. In such cases the physical features of the country might often be the first consideration, but other aspects of the survey would soon show the relationship between the geographical background and human life and activities.

In either rural or urban districts, a parish might be taken as the survey area, with the site and age of the church as a starting point. Here the physical background may have great importance in determining the original site of the village and influencing its growth and development. Courses of parish boundaries, which often follow natural features or sometimes very old roads or trackways that existed before the parish was defined, may suggest interesting historical and geographical problems, and these boundaries should be followed round on foot.

Study of the spread of buildings and increase in population within the parish is often due, also, to geographical position and to communications with the outside world, as well as to economic factors. Old maps and documents, if available, may here be used to supplement our observations and tell us the sizes and shapes of the settlement at different periods of its history, and a geological map may help to explain the influence of "background" on the general direction of growth. Water-supply, possibilities of new industries, communications with the outside world, all count, and such studies might well be accompanied by a graph showing increase or decrease of population compiled from census returns. But the variations shown here must not be left unexplained, and any historical records should, if possible, be checked by observations in the field. The present occupations of the inhabitants of the parish, whether agriculture, industry, trade, catering for tourists, mining or quarrying, may be compared with the traditional occupations of the district. In explaining such changes, local means of transport for men and for produce, throughout history, should be taken into account.

It is possible to take one centre of activity such as a seaport (Plate XI), or a river crossing, or a mine, or large farm as the unit of study and to consider its origin, history and probable future in connexion with its environment. Such a study would include a great variety of facts and observations which could eventually be arranged in logical order, and might well include the record of any inhabitant of the district who has left a mark and has had a decisive influence on its history. Especially in urban areas the work might centre round some industry and the survey could work backwards to deal with its origin and outwards to consider its raw materials and markets. The factory should, of course, be visited and its work seen in all stages. Here, again, communications are important and bring us back to the physical features of a larger district. In a large built-up area, the natural background is often difficult to trace, but even there, if contours are traced from the local 6 in. or $2\frac{1}{2}$ in. map the general relief of the land can be found. Such a physical map of a large city sometimes throws unexpected light on the subject. In some urban areas, even as unpromising as that shown in Plate VIII, local surveys have begun with the study of names of streets and public houses, which may date different periods of growth in the town, by their reference to historical events, to important people, or past industries, but, like all studies of place names, this can be very misleading and give rise to mere guessing if great care is not used. The chief style of architecture in any town or village can be related either to its history or to available building materials, or both. The latter case brings us back again to geology. And it must be realized that although under modern conditions the influence of local geology is less obvious, in tracing the *origin* of any settlement the question of water-supply can never be neglected and here some knowledge of geology is needed.

The radius of a given number of miles round the school might include within the area interesting problems and a good deal of variety and might ensure that all parts of the area could be reached by the surveyors, but in that case the boundaries would be arbitrary and difficult to deal with geographically.

If more than one distinctive type of country occurs in the chosen area, such as those above and below the escarpment in Plate I, much interest is added to the work. This opportunity to observe contrasts at close quarters should be helped by the careful study of maps of the area. Some of the chief uses of local maps will be discussed in the next chapter.

CHAPTER II

MAPS AND GEOGRAPHICAL APPLIANCES AS AIDS TO LOCAL SURVEY

ALTHOUGH local surveys should start with careful preliminary views of the country to be studied, and should be based throughout on first-hand observation, certain "tools" are needed for this as for any other work. Their use should be understood from the beginning and skill in applying them should be practised so that they can be used to advantage when needed.

The reading of maps, of the thermometer, rain-gauge and compass, the making of graphs, neat drawing and the power of clear description are all important, but the student should realize that all these are merely means to an end and not ends in themselves.

Map-reading

In getting to know and understand local features, whether in an urban or rural district, maps are the most helpful "tools" and practice in map-reading is essential, just as learning to read music accurately is essential in order to become a good performer or conductor. Therefore from the beginning local surveyors should have at hand, for constant reference, sheets of the local Ordnance Survey maps on the scales of 1 : 63360 and 1 : 10560 and of the 1 : 25,000 if published. Moreover, when maps are competently used in the study of one district, their importance and interest is stressed by comparisons with what is shown by such maps of other districts known to teacher or pupils. Probably an atlas will have been used in school geography lessons and so scholars will have some idea of the meaning of small-scale maps; moreover during and since the war, the general public has become familiar with sketch maps of places "in the news," though these maps, to be understood, should be considered as part of a larger region. It is also true that many people have used Ordnance Survey maps when walking and motoring, but often merely to find the way from place to place, and have afterwards realized how little of the country they have seen or remembered! Although the symbols used on Ordnance Survey maps are often taught in schools, these wonderful publications are really too full of information for a beginner to understand, until they are used out of doors and applied to the study of familiar country. Maps when rightly used can show and explain more of the country than can be seen from any one position.

Maps of the same district but on different scales, such as those of $\frac{1}{4}$ in., $\frac{1}{2}$ in., 1 in., $2\frac{1}{2}$ in. or 6 in. to the mile, should be compared. They are needed for different purposes, and students should find out what scale can be most helpful in the district to be explored.

The "natural scale" of these maps should be learned at once. They represent the number of units in the field corresponding to one unit on paper. For instance, if one inch on a map is represented by 63,360 inches on the ground, we say that the map is on 1 : 63,360 or 1 in. to a mile. We therefore find that 1 : 126,720 $= \frac{1}{2}$ in. to a mile, 1 : 25,000 $= 2\frac{1}{2}$ in. to a mile (approx.) and 1 : 10,560 $= 6$ in. to a mile, and so on.

Practical experience out of doors with such maps helps students to understand and realize features referred to in lessons on general geography or statements in newspapers when distances are described in miles or acres, or heights above sea-level or widths of rivers in feet, for instance. If such measurements shown on the maps of a well-known district can be checked out of doors, much confusion may be avoided. It is worth while in an early stage of the work to find and measure some standard distances on local maps, and to note their appearance in the field for comparison elsewhere.

The 1 : 63,360 or 1 in. map is perhaps the most familiar to the general public and the most easily obtainable from shops. Parts of it are reproduced here as Maps 2, 3 and 5 (facing pp. 24, 25 and 38).

The 1 : 10,560 or 6 in. maps can be obtained for any part of England from agents of the Ordnance Survey. The sheets are numbered by counties. Part of sheet Gloucestershire 34 is shown in this book on Map 1 (facing page 16).

Other scales, larger or smaller than these, are less frequently used but may be needed in certain districts or for special studies.

Many survey groups may want to use the new series, 1 : 25,000 (or approximately $2\frac{1}{2}$ in. to a mile) now being gradually published in a "Provisional Edition" based on the old 6 in. Ordnance Survey map, with certain additions. These sheets like those of the latest editions of the 1 in. maps, show the "National Grid" which is planned for finding the exact position of any point in the country. Lines are drawn parallel and at right angles to a N–S line, and form squares with sides of 10 kilometres, 1 kilometre or 100 metres (not yards or inches), according to the scale of the map.

On the 1 in. map these lines are spaced and numbered at kilometre intervals, and each of the squares (though of course smaller on the paper) covers the same area of country as those on the 1:25,000 maps. More exact references are obtained by estimating tenths between grid lines, counting from the west and south of the squares. Examples of such measurements are given on the margin of the maps reproduced here.

Compare Map 6 (page 39) with Map 2 (page 24): in addition to its scale being larger, some of the symbols are different. In Map 6, while water is still blue the roads and contours are brown, houses grey (though public buildings are black), and the character of the shore-line and cliffs is shown in some detail. In these new maps contours are at intervals of 25 feet instead of the 50 feet interval of the 1 in. maps. Woodlands are grey, not green.

As a rule, maps on large scales such as 6 in. or even 25 in. to a mile are best for the younger pupils who can at once locate their home or school building and enjoy finding familiar fields, streets or houses on the map. And for a detailed study of a small area the 6 in. map is essential for older students, too.

Maps on Scale of 6 in. to 1 mile

Map 1 (facing page 16) is reproduced from the 6 in. Ordnance Survey map which is published in whole or quarter sheets, the latter covering an area of 6 square miles. In Map 1, parts of two quarter-sheets are combined. What can we learn from it?

Contour lines, being coloured red, are the most important features. Surveyed at every 100 feet, they show the shapes as well as the heights of important features of the landscape.

Gradients of the hillsides and of certain roads can thus be estimated, though for detailed work some "filling-in" between contour lines is needed, and the figures showing "spot-heights" and "bench-marks" (measured heights above sea-level) should be noted. They are useful when cross-country sections are made. The scenery of part of this district is shown in Plate I (facing page 12). It is helpful if, at an early stage in work on any 6 in. map, the student colours all surface water (rivers and streams, ponds and springs) in blue. Streams can be distinguished from field boundaries by the little arrows showing the direction in which the water flows.

The symbols on the margin of the map the student is using should be learnt, including the types of printing illustrating various areas, towns, and also objects dating from different periods of history (prehistoric, Roman, and medieval). So should symbols showing where certain types of vegetation, woodland, whether coniferous or deciduous, marsh, or heath country occur. These should be visited and the appearance of such vegetation described. Methods of showing roads and footpaths should be noted, sites of past and present industries found and visited, and any changes should be referred to the last revision of the map, the date of which must always be borne in mind.

These maps show sufficient detail in a small area for almost every feature to be checked at first-hand and the fact that every isolated building or, in cities, groups of buildings in streets or squares is shown, enables the student to see and record the extent and direction of the growth of a settlement.

If the contour lines on Map 1 are examined, and the streams defined in blue, an idea of the landforms in this district will be gained. It will be seen that the land drops abruptly from an upland region in the south to a lowland in the north. The map therefore includes two types of country. Woods clothe the steeper slopes, springs rise, approximately, on the boundary between the two regions, fields are small, houses scattered and the lettering tells you of relics of several periods of history. But what does the region *look like*? Even a very skilled map-reader will need the evidence of his own eyes or a photograph to answer this question.

(E.446)

PLATE I. PART OF THE COTSWOLD ESCARPMENT

PLATE II. PART OF A COTSWOLD VALLEY
(Looking W.)

PLATE III. COTSWOLD VILLAGE ON A HILLSIDE
(Looking E.S.E.)

Small Scale Maps

The small area shown on the 6 in. map cannot be understood unless it is considered as part of a larger whole. Maps on scales of $\frac{1}{4}$ in., $\frac{1}{2}$ in. or 1 in. to the mile show the main trends of hills, the general aspects of slopes, the character of the larger rivers (whether straight or winding, in a valley or on a floodplain) and may guide us to their source or mouth. They may also tell something of the destinations of roads, canals, or railways passing through the district. The 1 in. O.S. map, that most often used on holidays, gives us a good idea of the physical background and some of man's activities. How can this help us in a "local survey"?

Map 2 (facing page 13) shows an area of about 32 square miles, which includes that shown in Map 1. As more colour is used the chief features stand out more clearly than in Map 1, although on a smaller scale. Map 2 shows that the scarp which separates the two chief geographical regions is steeper towards the top, and its line is broken by a spur projecting northwards and flanked on either side by bays in which northward-flowing streams rise. Some of these are gathered up by the reservoir which appears in both maps and in Plate I. The north-west of Map 2 shows a feature not included in Map 1, a large city. Its area should be compared with the ground covered by the neighbouring villages, bearing in mind that, like most towns, it has spread considerably since the map was last revised.

The flat or gently undulating country on the north should be contrasted with the uplands on the south, where less surface water and more contours are found. It will be seen that Maps 1 and 2 supplement each other, each emphasizing certain features less prominent in the other, while Map 2 supplies the setting of Map 1.

In some districts, survey groups may be able to use the new Ordnance Survey maps on the scale of approximately $2\frac{1}{2}$ in. to a mile (1 : 25,000) (as in Map 6, facing page 39), in addition to those described above, combining and supplementing their special uses. In the new maps the contour lines (in brown) are shown for every 25 feet, so physical features stand out in some detail. Field and parish boundaries are faintly marked; town plans are easy to follow. The grid-lines are distinct and therefore any particular spot is easily found, but they may be disturbing to the general impression of the geography of the area.

It is important, therefore, at the outset of a survey, to decide on the best scale for maps to be used as the basis of the work. This will depend partly on the nature of the district and partly on the possibilities of movement within it in order to see it satisfactorily. While the 6 in. and $2\frac{1}{2}$ in. maps show detail, the general trend of the more important physical features and network of communications can best be studied on the 1 in. or $\frac{1}{2}$ in. scales. The symbols on the borders of any maps used should be learnt thoroughly as soon as possible.

The maps in this book show examples of different types of country on different scales and will be studied with the appropriate plates.

Physical Features on Maps

It may be noted that maps of the sea-coast include special features. Thus the steepness of cliffs cannot always be shown by contours, which there coincide, so the lines are sometimes cut off short against the "precipice" (Map 5, facing page 38). Special symbols are used as for different types of shores. Submarine contours, spaced by fathoms instead of feet, are important in showing features affecting shipping which cannot be observed at first-hand.

In some maps, methods of showing relief other than by contour lines should also be studied. "Hachures" on certain maps are lines running down a slope, thicker and closer together where steepness increases. When the scale of the map is sufficiently large these hachures can show sudden steepness and broken ground, but they tend to hide other features and lettering. Another way of showing relief is by shading as if the light were falling on the landscape from the north-west. This does not indicate the gradient, but slopes facing north-west will be light and those facing south-east will be in shadow. In some maps shading is combined with colour; in others the spaces between the contours are tinted in different shades or colours. Students should compare the methods and information used in post-war editions of the Ordnance Survey maps, with previous editions of these maps.

Problems of Visibility

When contour lines are closer at the top of a slope than below, a concave slope is represented, and there objects can be seen from above. If the lines are closer below, the curve of the slope is convex and, as frequently seen on a spur, objects at the foot of the hill would be invisible from the top. This can, of course, be observed in the field, but the actual degree of slope and the positions of invisible objects can be checked on the map if the students have had any experience of surveying. Gradients which vary in degree between the surveyed contours can be measured by clinometer or Abney level and positions can be found by prismatic compass or plane table, but this specialized branch of the subject may well be left to a later stage in the work. Aspects of slopes, and consequently relative amounts of sunshine, should however be considered in relation to agriculture and sites of buildings.

Geological Maps

The Ordnance Survey map of 1 in. to a mile has the advantage that the Geological Survey map was published on the same scale. At present, geological maps are almost unobtainable, but they are gradually being reprinted and, when not available otherwise, they may perhaps be seen in many public libraries.

They should be consulted by the teacher and older scholars early in the work, as a general idea of the rock structure of the district is very important. Detailed work on this subject needs practice, but it should be realized at once that colours used on these maps represent *periods of geological time* and not necessarily kinds of rock, although in some cases (e.g. chalk) these would be the same. But clay, limestone, sand or sandstone may each date from several periods. The order of these geological periods is shown in a table on the border of the geological maps, the older rocks at the bottom.

An area chosen for survey may contain only one kind of rock of only one geological period. Here, the scenery is likely to be of one type throughout and perhaps rather monotonous. In some areas, however, such as that in Map 1, three or four distinct types of rock, belonging to about eight geological periods, are found, exposed either on the surface or in section. These give great variety and interest to the scenery, vegetation and building materials, and in the district shown in Map 1 produce springs at several different altitudes where porous rock lies over clay which holds up water. A geological map, read aright, would indicate where springs might be expected. Landslips might occur in such country. A cliff in Plate VII shows three geological strata exposed. It may also be noted here that the geological map helps to account for the sites of certain local industries, such as mines and quarries, certain watermills, reservoirs and the position of villages and old houses.

The use of a compass is worth learning, for "setting" a map correctly in country not well known, and an interesting panorama might be drawn of a wide view, the positions of landmarks fixed by compass bearings. Even beginners or younger pupils can find, by compass, the directions of the sun, or of shadows, and relate them to the time of day. If a prismatic compass and level are used in more advanced and detailed surveys, additional contour lines can be added to those published on the map, and interest is added to the more technical lessons in surveying if they can be used to clear up geographical problems.

Photographs Taken From the Air

It may be found that photographs from the air (Plate XII) are useful in teaching map-reading. Certain features may be more intelligible in them than in a map and may be seen more clearly than from a position on the ground. It is good practice to use aerial photographs *with* a map and to try to find the position above which the photograph was taken. Buildings, roads and paths, field boundaries, and, of course, a coast-line such as that in Map 6 show clearly from the air, but with such foreshortening of physical features that important landmarks are often difficult to identify. In Plate XII (facing page 51), rows of houses with gardens are seen in the foreground and the western part of the harbour shown in Map 6 is seen in the centre, but the photograph (looking south-west) gives no idea of the height and steepness of the cliff behind the port, and the valley in the foreground of the picture is less defined than in Map 6. For children, or beginners in map-reading, air photographs may be misleading unless carefully explained and checked in the field, as they represent a point of view which comparatively few people can hope to see.

In air photographs, as in those taken from the ground, directions of shadows are significant, for instance the scene in Plate XII (page 51) on the south-east coast, was obviously photographed in the early afternoon. If your local survey takes place in a district where archaeological discoveries have been made from the air, it would be interesting if the pictures in question could be obtained and the ground studied at first-hand.

Climate and Weather

All local surveys should include references to these. Thermometer and rain-gauge are useful if uninterrupted records can be kept over long periods. Such records can be very dull if unrelated to a definite problem, but the meteorological work gains a new meaning if undertaken by a group of students or a school which can exchange records with another group working in a region with different land relief and weather conditions, or which can relate observations to problems of agriculture or gardening. The records, too, may be of use in future work. A rainfall map of the area, constructed from averages of local records, often tallies with local relief of land in a remarkable manner. Frost records can be related to aspects of slopes and directions of prevailing winds, and show the conditions on valley-sides known as "inversion of temperature." Such "practical" work impresses the student with the value of the thermometer and rain-gauge in a geographical study.

SOME PROBLEMS AND EXPERIMENTS

(Exercises 1-4 are the most suitable for beginners and younger students)

1. Study your local Ordnance Survey Maps, scales 1 : 63,360 or 1 : 25,000, and find your position. Note the hills, rivers, roads, and important buildings near. List or mark those that you personally have seen.

2. Learn the points of the compass. Set the map, the top margin towards the north. Note the compass bearings on the chief features of the district, both on the map and out of doors.

3. Look at the sheets of the 6 in. map (1 : 10,560), which cover the area to be studied in detail. Find your position and the compass bearing on the same objects located in the 1 in. map. Note how the objects are shown on the maps of different scales.

4. Study and memorize the symbols shown on the margins of different maps, and use them when drawing maps of your own.

5. Look at Map 2 (page 24), which shows two types of country. Find a lowland and an upland area in it, and the highest point above sea-level. What course is taken by the natural boundary between the two types of country? Compare the altitudes (highest and lowest) above sea-level with those in your district.

6. In which part of Map 1 (page 16) do you find the steepest slopes? Are contour lines nearer together on the upper or lower slopes? Do they resemble those in your district in this respect? Trace contour lines from your local 6-in. map and colour the spaces between them, thus making a relief map.

7. Find in Maps 1 and 2 the places where contour lines show (a) a spur, (b) a bay, (c) a dry valley, (d) a gap where roads meet. Find these features in Plate I (page 12), Plate II (page 13). Have you any such features in your own district?

8. Find, in Map 2, a slope which is concave, where objects can be seen from above, and one which is convex, where objects are invisible from above. Make graphs to show gradients of these slopes. Which parts of Maps 3 and 5 (pages 25 and 38) would be invisible in Plates IV and V (pages 20 and 21)?

9. In what part of Map 2 is there the most dense network of streams? What does this tell you of the underlying rocks? Make a tracing of the streams in your district, noting where they are most plentiful and meander most widely.

10. On Maps 1 and 2, and on your local maps, note methods of showing roads, fenced and unfenced; bridle-paths and footpaths, whether they keep to high or low ground, tend to follow streams or cross them. Trace the roads, railways, and canals (if any) in your area, and place this tracing over a map of physical features, noting any apparent connexion.

(N.B. In all tracings, mark the corners of maps so that they can be placed accurately one over the other.)

Make a graph to show the gradient of any important road, using altitudes shown by contour lines, spot heights, and bench marks.

11. On Maps 1 and 2 note the positions of woodland. Does it occur on steep slopes or level ground? How many types of vegetation can you find on the map? How do these compare with your district?

12. Note the sites of antiquities. Map 2 shows prehistoric tumuli, or barrows, remains of a pre-Roman camp, a Roman villa and road, a house of historic interest, disused quarries and mills. Note the sites of these as shown on other maps in this book, or in maps of your district.

13. Note the sites of farms and villages in relation to springs, which should be marked on your tracings of surface water. Many of those shown in Map 1 supply drinking water. Note the reservoir supplying the neighbouring town. Compare these with your local water supply.

14. On Map 2 note the sizes of villages and of the large city in the north-west corner. Compare these with areas of settlements on your local map. Note any growth of towns or villages which you may observe and which has taken place since the last revision of the map.

15. Give the reference numbers of the National Grid of the site of your own village or town in your local map.

CHAPTER III

APPROACH TO LOCAL SURVEY THROUGH A VISUAL IMPRESSION

THE most obvious and attractive approach to the study of any locality is through its "scenery"—that seen at first-hand. The first viewpoint should be carefully chosen for its power to inspire beginners with a wish to find reasons for what they see, and they should rid their minds of the idea that "scenery" must be beautiful or spectacular. A point from which a large expanse of country can be seen is desirable—the top of a hill, or a sea cliff, or church tower, or a bridge, or even a vista looking down a long straight street. The photographs of different types of country reproduced in this book as examples which might be studied include some such views, but it is possible to start a survey without this advantage.

Types of Country

Assuming that the leader of the survey group and, it is hoped, some of the other members, have realized how maps can be used in their work, and can read them sufficiently well to use them when needed, we will now take a preliminary look at the types of country illustrated here. They are very varied, and not all of them are beautiful or even at first sight interesting, Some such first impressions, as in Plates VIII and IX, might even be discouraging to would-be surveyors. But it is our aim to find something in each of them which would lead on to studies of some interest.

Contrasts. Upland and Lowland. Influences of Physical Geography on Human Activities

Let us begin with Plate I (page 12). We have maps of this district on two scales which we can consult to supplement what we can see before us (Maps 1 and 2). The photographer stood on high ground, irregular and broken in the foreground, looking over a broad plain, with low hills beyond. The small shadows suggest that it was near midday. (If we knew the exact time when the photograph was taken we could deduce from the shadows the direction of the view.) A strip of woodland or scrub is just below the photographer and similarly covers the top of the spur on the left side of the picture, which projects like a promontory over the plain, partly behind a sheet of water (a reservoir) in the middle distance. The upper slopes of the spur are steeper than those below. In the far distance is a line of mist indicating the course of a wide river and its flood-plain. Note that the country is mainly grassland, divided into small fields of irregular shapes by hedgerows with trees of various kinds. The lower ground is crossed by deep little gullies containing tiny streams which rise in the scarp-face below us and, cutting into its lower slopes, flow away towards the mist-covered distant river.

You now need your maps. Plate I is taken from the spot marked with a red cross on Map 1 (page 16) looking west. Find the same spot in Map 2 (page 24). The reservoir and the northward-pointing spur are recognized at once. Note how the spacing of the contour lines suggests the gradients seen in the picture. Look at what fields, and which buildings shown on the map, are seen in the view, and which are invisible. The distant hills are beyond the boundary of the map, but a white patch beyond the reservoir indicates the roof of a factory marked in black north-west of the reservoir and south of the Roman road in Map 2. This map includes two very distinct types of country, at one of which we have been looking north-westwards. Let us now see what the country is like behind us. Plate II (page 13) looks westwards. The picture is taken from a point marked with a red cross in Map 2. The depression or notch in the ridge on the right of the picture is to be found on the left on the map. This is a feature of some importance. The contour lines compared with the view show that the scarp is lowest there, and the deeply cut valley in the foreground of the picture has reduced it to a narrow ridge. At this natural gap or "col" eight roads or trackways meet (some of them of great antiquity), either taking the line of least resistance in crossing from the plateau country to the vale below, or following the crest of the escarpment.

Plate III (page 13) shows another view of this plateau country, taken from about half a mile west of the red cross on

Plate IV. Derwentwater and Keswick

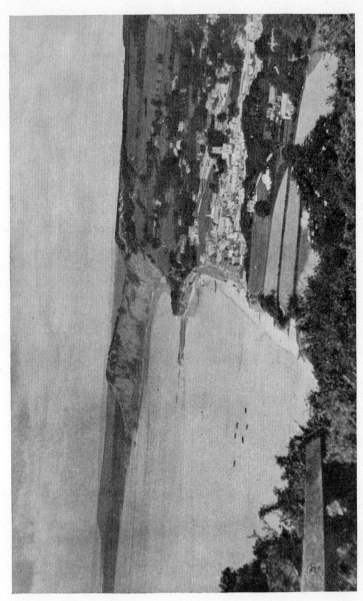

PLATE V. SIDMOUTH AND PART OF THE SOUTH DEVON COAST

Map 2 and looking south-east. So we see that on reaching the plateau from the north we have come from a country of hedgerows to that of stone walls (obviously more convenient where soil is thin and stone available) and to solidly built stone houses. This suggests that the rock of the district has changed since the clay-floored vale with its river mist was left behind. The architecture of the older buildings also changes abruptly about half-way up the scarp, although in places there is some overlapping of two styles. This is by no means the only district in England where building materials are closely related to geological boundaries. Of course this applies only to older buildings. New houses with the more modern building materials are not affected by changes in character of the underlying rocks. In making such studies the date of the map showing buildings should be noted and new buildings or new streets can be added to the map from personal observation.

Even in this rural district, the pictures show us something of man's activities in his natural background. The valley-side village in Plate III is small and the houses somewhat scattered. Some new bungalows, not shown on the map, have been built on the common. The site resembles that of many villages of this district, close to a good spring, on a belt of fertile soil. It is on one of the roads leading to the gap where the scarp is lowest. The limestone of the uplands is exposed in a quarry in the centre of the picture. The valley side is steep and grass covered, cultivated only in small patches annexed from the common and enclosed by stone walls. The picture indicates some of the dry valleys so common in limestone or chalk country—one begins near the surface of the plateau and finds its way down to the main valley on the left. The contours on the map are too far apart to show these dry valleys clearly, but when surveyed or sketched in detail they make an interesting pattern which completes that of the surface drainage. Their origin is rather controversial. The lane leading to the village is deeply sunk below the general level of the land, suggesting an old trackway. A closer view would show that the trees here are almost entirely beech, in contrast to the great variety of trees below the scarp in Plate I. Many have been felled since the war. The village in Plate III has changed remarkably little in recent years, whereas much of the lowland in Plate I is covered by buildings which have been put up since the area was mapped. Old photographs, if they can be dated, are useful in checking such changes.

Measurement of Distances seen in the Field

Before leaving this view it might be helpful to measure, on the maps, distances of certain landmarks that can be found in the pictures, in order to learn what objects at certain distances, e.g. 1 mile, 5 miles, 1000 yards, etc., look like in the field. Contours will thus show slopes of definite heights. But it must be remembered that weather conditions affect apparent distances, especially in hill country.

Some Problems to be Solved and Interests to be Investigated

Our preliminary glance at the country in Plates I, II and III therefore suggests certain problems that might be followed up. The reasons for two such distinct types of country should be investigated and for this some knowledge of their geological foundations will help. There is much scope for nature study in the woods, fields and common lands. The study of agriculture will be varied and interesting in this region of mixed farming which has a long history, and this again leads to the consideration of markets, and communications, old roads dating from Roman times, if not earlier, and modern routes. For the region is full of history, and although relics of the past cannot be recognized in the small photographs, the sites of many are shown on the maps in appropriate lettering, and these sites are closely connected with the physical background. The site of the village in Plate III can be looked at in connexion with its activities in past and present: forestry, farming and a former pottery industry which used local clay. The rapid growth of villages in the plain, Plate I, mainly to house workers in the factory there shown, is another line of research.

Mountain Country

We can next compare the views we have already studied with a first impression of Plate IV (page 20). The lake is the most striking feature, but cannot be considered apart from its surroundings. Here there is no level plateau but the uplands rise to separate peaks and ridges. The slopes are much steeper than those in Plates I and II, and the contours on Map 3 (page 25) should be studied after the view has been examined, and compared with those of Map 2 (page 24). The horizontal scale is the same. Compare the altitudes of the highest point shown on Maps 2 and 3 and the areas of water in Plates I and IV. Plate IV was taken from the point marked with a red cross in Map 3, looking east of south. The compact little town in the foreground on low ground at the foot of the lake is surrounded by fields with hedges in contrast to the bare open mountain slopes. It has evidently grown up at the meeting place of several natural routes through difficult country, such as the broad valleys converging on the lake, and an east-west route now used by a railway. This (shown on the map) is almost hidden from the view in the picture, but part of it can be seen in front of the large hotel in the foreground.

Such a view suggests at first sight that mountain farming (sheep) and the activities of a local market, perhaps quarrying and forestry and a "tourist industry" might be studied here, some of these activities largely depending on local geology and weather conditions.

Lowland Country

Plate IX shows country of a very different type. It might seem at first that this would provide a less exciting survey, but it has its own problems. The distant hill is much lower and of quite a different shape from those in Plates II and IV, and has a different origin. The picture suggests that the surface rock in the foreground may be softer and the soil deeper than in the areas looked at before. No sheep are seen here, but cattle graze near the water, the rising ground is cultivated and woodland covers part of the hill. Part of this hill is a public park, crowned with a war memorial which suggests that it can be seen from afar and may be the highest point in the district. The picture was taken at a height of 450 feet and the hill is only about 700 feet. The photographer was looking towards north of east, so the time of day can be found from the shadows, and the direction of the prevailing winds (evidently strong here) from the bent tree trunks. Agriculture, with a study of soils, would be the most obvious line of study here. The natural vegetation, too, would probably vary with the soils. The water in the foreground is part of a reservoir, with all that that implies.

An Urban Area

Then there is the somewhat discouraging view shown in Plate VIII, such an area in which many would-be local surveyors may find themselves. What can be done there? The factory chimneys are, of course, the outstanding features here, and there is much useful and interesting work to be done in studying an important industry, its raw materials and the uses made of its products. But much of this work must be done by working out statistics and by inquiries, and, good training as such studies may be, we are here more concerned with the value of first-hand observation. So in a scene such as Plate VIII the distances of the various chimneys and land-marks can be measured on a large scale map, their heights estimated, and the direction of the smoke from day to day may be the basis for meteorological observations.

And then there is the open space in the foreground. What is the soil like and what weeds grow on it? Beginnings of "nature study," with lists and drawings of these plants and any insects found, may be made even here. In many spaces opened due to bombing, remains of long past ages have been found. These should be at once reported to someone who can identify them accurately, such as the curator of a museum, or a local archaeologist. Look at the surrounding buildings and try to find out their date. Compare them with any now being built, sketch both and note any improvements. The names of streets if added to the map may be some clue to the period when the town developed, and perhaps to its former activities.

The Use of Photographs

Coastal problems are dealt with in Chapter VII, but readers can now take a preliminary glance at Plates V, X and XI (pages 21, 50 and 51), and consider what the relation between physical background and human activities in such "scenery" may be.

It is important to remember, however, that maps and even recent photographs cannot take the place of a view at first-hand, though they may be very useful in choosing such a view for the beginning of a study in the field. The photograph of a

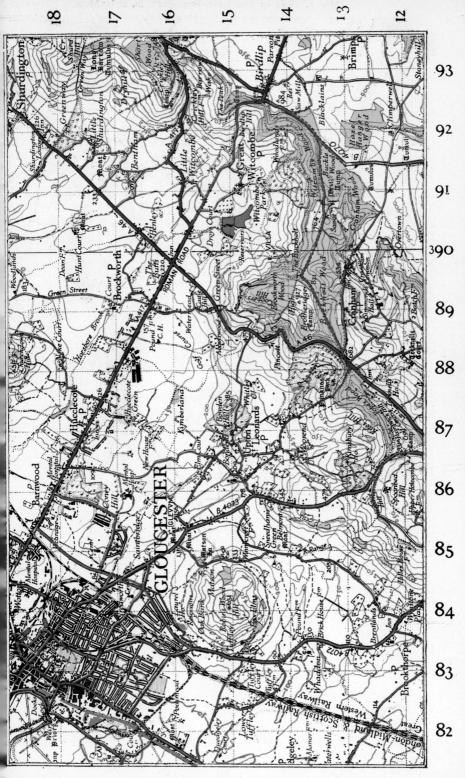

MAP 3. PART OF THE LAKE DISTRICT: 1 IN. TO 1 MILE

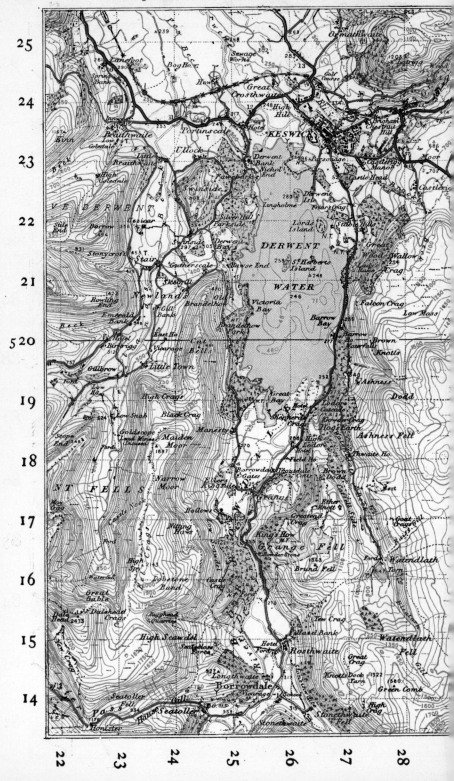

distant view will not tell you the colour of the soils or the uses made of the land or the varieties of trees and of flowering plants. The flora in the areas in Plates III and IV, for instance, are quite different and both add much to the beauty and interest of the locality. Buildings, too, must be observed in detail and it is obvious how many houses, especially the older ones, give character to a landscape. Then, movement of traffic along a road or railway is important and a photograph only gives one moment of it.

Air photographs such as Plate XII are useful in some respects and may help beginners in map-reading, but are of doubtful value for children exploring a district, as they show a landscape so much foreshortened as to seem unreal to those who cannot see it from that point of view. So these pictures should be used only to show what cannot be seen otherwise, or should be supplemented by pictures taken on the ground.

Assuming, then, that you are able to begin by looking at a wide expanse of country and to note any conspicuous features, the party might well discuss the scene as such, whether it is beautiful or ugly, and why, how much its appearance is due to natural features or to man's work, whether it has been spoiled or improved by recent developments and what is likely to happen in future. Note, on the map, those features which are most striking and shade those areas which are invisible from your viewpoint. Why are they hidden and how does the map explain country that you cannot see? Do not be discouraged if the first view of the district to be surveyed is something like Plate VIII, or even Plate IX. Though they look unpromising there are many possibilities in both, though they may have to be approached rather differently from studies of the areas in Plates III, IV and V. But even in the case of Plate VIII, observation of the general aspect of the area should come before more detailed investigation.

The Next Step

Having, then, learned something of the chief characteristics of your district, it is time to decide on the aspects of the subject that most appeal to you for further study. Investigations might be divided among the survey group or class for independent research and the results pooled later on by someone who can work them up into a logical sequence, or the exploring party might prefer to work together and follow up one line of study at a time. This choice depends on the attainments and experience of the surveyors and on the district in which they are to work.

In the sample districts which we have been considering we have suggested that rock structure is of immense importance and in the next chapter we will consider an approach to local study through an elementary study of geology (or, rather, that aspect of it known as the study of land-forms or geomorphology) and see where that will take us. We can start by considering either a spectacular landscape such as that in Plate IV, or one with an apparently unimportant detail only, as the rock in Plate VI.

SOME PROBLEMS AND EXPERIMENTS

(Exercises 1–4 are the most suitable for beginners and younger students)

1. Find a good viewpoint if possible and decide which are the most important features in it. Look at these with local maps. Note any objects of interest shown on your map but invisible from where you stand. Write a description of the chief physical features seen from your viewpoint.

2. Learn the points of the compass, how to find your bearings and how to set a map correctly. Note the time of day and direction of shadows.

3. Make a tracing from your local map of all surface water (ponds, streams, springs) distinguishing those that you have personally seen. Mark the water in blue, and contour lines in red.

4. Note the chief uses made of the land. Where it is arable note the crops grown, distinguish temporary from permanent grassland, and record the animals seen. Note orchards and gardens. Look at the colour of the soil, and note whether it is dry or sticky. Mark on your 6 in. map what you have personally seen in each field, and the date when these observations were made.

5. List the weeds found in field or garden, noting the kind of soil and the aspect of the slope, if any.

6. Enter on your map the kinds of field boundaries—whether walls, hedges, wire fences, earthbanks, etc. What trees grow in the hedges?

7. What signs of man's activity can you see (a) from your viewpoint, (b) when walking over the district? Note any sites of industry no longer active. Compare any present sites of industry with these.

8. Look at the date of the last revision of your local map. Mark, from personal observation, the new houses and streets which have been made since then. Relate these to physical features.

9. Choose a small area including, if possible, varied scenery and colour. Mark on the 6 in. map all houses, according to the building materials used.

10. Try to find out, by comparing your local maps and tracings, and by observations in the field, any reasons for sites of settlements in your district. Draw sketch maps to illustrate your ideas and discoveries.

CHAPTER IV

APPROACH THROUGH STUDY OF LAND-FORMS AND GEOLOGY

IN many districts the structure of the rocks and resulting scenery is so striking that "surveyors" may wish to start their work with study of these. This is most likely to happen in mountain and hill country, such as that in Plates I, II and IV, or on the sea coast (Plates VI and X), but geology can also play an important part in the study of lowland country (Plate IX), and may arouse interest in a district which at first sight seems uninteresting.

Main Classes of Rocks

Before starting a survey from this angle, teachers or survey leaders should know something of the main classes of rocks, their origins and most characteristic features. It is important that even beginners should recognize their local rocks in the field, so that they can mark exposures of them on the 6 in. map. A visit to a museum, where the group might learn the appearance of some of the more important local rocks, would help. For instance, it is important to know whether the district includes examples of the following main classes of rock, and where.

Igneous Rocks were once in a molten condition underground, and while cooling slowly, at a great depth, had time to separate out into crystals in the process. These are mainly found in wild hill country in the north and west of Britain and are exposed on parts of the coast of Cornwall (Plate VI, page 42). Mineral veins are found in such rocks, sometimes giving rise to mining, and it is an impressive thought that even high mountains, if formed of granite or other crystalline rocks, were once covered by an immense thickness of other material, now removed by erosion throughout many ages. These, which cooled below the surface, are called Plutonic rocks after the Greek god, Pluto, who was thought to live underground. Volcanic rocks (rare in Britain) are also igneous, but when molten and hot escaped through vents on to the land surface and cooled too quickly (in the open air) to form crystals. They are often hard and smooth, but sometimes perforated with tiny holes through which steam escaped. A hill formed of very ancient volcanic rock is on the extreme left of Plate IV.

Sedimentary Rocks, most common in England, were originally spread as sediments under water, being afterwards tilted, folded, or even fractured by geological "faults," and, in many cases, stripped bare of the material formed in later periods which once covered them. Sedimentary rocks may be limestone or chalk, sand, sandstone, or clay, and should be recognized. Many districts contain more than one of these, even in such a small area as that shown in Maps 1 and 2. The different qualities of these rocks influence scenery, and have marked effects on the vegetation which grows on each. Their influence on local architecture is obvious. Limestones of various kinds, flint (from chalk), sandstone, and also bricks from clay, have been used for older buildings where they occur. The colour, hardness and jointing of such rocks can be seen in quarries, cuttings and sea-cliffs. A quarry (now disused), high up on the spur in Plate I, shows grey limestone above sand with clay below. Such variety accounts for the different gradients on the end of the spur. The belt of beechwood approximately coincides with the limestone exposure. The cliffs in Plate V show, in the field, a spectacular series of differently coloured strata, and in the enlargement on Plate VII of the highest peak of the coastline, three of these can be distinguished.

Coal Measures

Another type of sedimentary rock deserves special attention as it produces coal. Many considerations relating to coal are now so much discussed that scholars in or near a colliery district should find interest in its origin. We learn that "the British coal measures consist of a series of sandstones, clays, coal and occasional beds of limestone, which are together from 8000 to 12,000 feet in thickness, yet all the members of this series were laid down at sea-level. Throughout the formation of coal measures the ground must have been sinking at the same rate as the deposition of the rocks . . . . That many of the coal seams were laid down in the forests where the trees grew is shown by the coal seams often resting on beds of fire-clay that served as forest soil, for the roots are still found in these under-clays, and the stumps of trees rise up from the fire-clay into the overlying seams of coal."*

The coal itself, found in "seams" of varying thickness, is made of decayed and compressed vegetation of many ages ago. It has been suggested that the forests of those times grew under tropical conditions, but that some of the processes which turned them into coal are acting on present-day peat bogs. However that may be, coal was formed in several periods of geological history. Near the limestones of the north of England, and in Gloucestershire, we mine that of the Late Carboniferous period.

Obviously, in a colliery district, study of the history of coal and of the rocks which separate the seams will lead to the complex economic problems of the coal industry, in which, however, the position, thickness and dip of the seams should not be forgotten. A mine should be visited if permission can be obtained.

Then there are the surface features of the district and the effects on vegetation and farming of the different rocks in the coal measure series which come to the surface. Modifications of the scenery due to slag heaps, and sites, sizes and layout of mining villages should be noted. Problems connected with new methods of open-cast mining lead to the question of why coal is found near the surface in some districts and so far under-ground or even under the sea, in others. And so we come back to geology!

In addition to the classes of Igneous and Sedimentary rocks, there is a class known as Metamorphic, a word which implies a change in the character of these rocks since their formation. They have been subjected to strains and stresses underground which set up great pressure and great subterranean heat. Rocks within reach were thus "baked," compressed, folded or split until their original form was lost and their fossils destroyed. In this way, limestone has been turned into marble, sand into a kind of hard sandstone called quartzite, and clay into slate. Useful materials therefore may be found among

* *Geology of To-day* by J. W. Gregory.

the metamorphic rocks which produce such wild scenery as that on the right of the lake in Plate IV. Slate quarries are not far away, in the extreme south-west corner of Map 3. Compare the appearance of the hills on the right of the lake with those of old volcanic rock on the left.

Many varieties of rock are difficult to recognize but their positions can be found on a geological map and specimens can be sent to a museum to be identified. In a local survey rocks are chiefly of interest for the building materials and minerals found in them, as well as for the scenery they produce.

Fossils

These are found in Sedimentary rocks and show something of the life of the times when these deposits were laid down. Children like to collect them but the advanced study of fossils is a very specialized one and does not lead on directly to the work of a local survey.

But it is useful if even beginners can record on a map the position of any local rock seen in section, and notice where the colour and quality of the rock changes, and whether the soil and vegetation change at the same place. And because geological maps are so scarce at present, personal observations of this kind are specially valuable.

Earth Sculpture

Having come to some conclusion about what sort of rock forms our district, we can next study how it has been shaped into the present-day scenery, by rain and streams, by frost or by the sea. These different processes act differently according to the hardness, porosity or steepness of the rock on which they work. The climate also counts for much.

Landslides may result when a porous rock such as limestone or gravel, dipping in a certain direction, gets waterlogged after a rainy period and slides down in hummocky masses over an impervious clay floor. Such a landslip stretches for several miles along the base of the cliff in Map 5 and part of it appears on the extreme right of Plate V, below where the photographer stood. Another occurred beyond the spur in Plate I, where limestone lies above impervious clay, in the extreme south-west corner of Map 1.

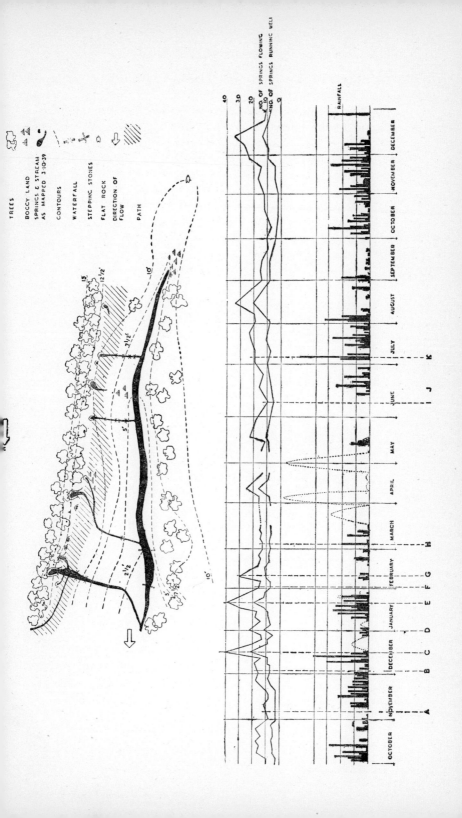

TREES

BOGGY LAND

SPRINGS & STREAM
AS MAPPED 3·10·39

CONTOURS

WATERFALL

STEPPING STONES

FLAT ROCK

DIRECTION OF
FLOW

PATH

NO OF SPRINGS FLOWING
NO OF SPRINGS RUNNING WELL

RAINFALL

OCTOBER | NOVEMBER | DECEMBER | JANUARY | FEBRUARY | MARCH | APRIL | MAY | JUNE | JULY | AUGUST | SEPTEMBER | OCTOBER | NOVEMBER | DECEMBER

Springs

It is well known that a spring or springs may flow out at or near the junction between a waterlogged porous rock and an underlying impervious formation. It will be found that such springs have had, throughout history, much influence on the sites of settlements. A line of springs, not far from a line of villages, is found below many escarpments of porous rock. Some springs are not permanent, and their outflow varies with the amount of water accumulated during a spell of recent rainfall, and they sometimes fail altogether after a drought, especially in limestone or chalk country. Map 4 represents some work done by a student at the head of the valley shown in Plates II and III. The springs are where Cranham wood is named in Map 2. They emerge on a valley-side near the base of Inferior Oolite limestone above Upper Lias clay. "Rainfall pillars" show results of daily readings from a rain-gauge near. The line of springs varies in number from 3 to 40 according to the preceding weather—they were counted twice a week and the number of those flowing were plotted in the graph. This shows that a steady, even if not excessive, rainfall over several days or weeks produces more springs than one day's very heavy rain. The springs, moreover, can be seen enlarging the little tunnels through which they flow, and so gradually cutting back the hillside—an object lesson in the "headward erosion" of streams, so difficult to explain on paper. Such work carried on over a considerable period is an excellent training in observation and accuracy in studying land-forms.

Natural caverns are found in some limestone districts, due to erosion by underground water along joints in the rock, and streams often run for miles underground before appearing on the surface. The extent and character of these caves and subterranean rivers is a fascinating subject to many people; an additional interest is the fact that remains of early man and animals have been found near entrances of certain caves. But children should be forbidden to explore caves or disused quarries or old mines unless accompanied by an adult with some experience.

Erosion by surface water is not limited to certain kinds of rock, but is most active where streams have a steep fall, currents are strong, and the rock not too hard. Most of the erosion of stream-beds is done by stones and gravel carried or rolled along by water in flood-time. The work of these "tools" can be watched when water has risen after heavy rain in hill country. So can the building up of the stream-bed when the load is dropped as the current slackens.

The network of streams is usually denser on a clay surface than on porous rock, such as limestone, chalk, or sand, where rain sinks below the surface and collects as in a sponge. Therefore the drainage pattern, if traced from a 6 in. map, gives a clue to the distribution of porous and impervious rock (which should, however, be checked in the field) and so to the distribution of settlements.

Dry valleys, such as that in Plate XII, often occur on porous rock, in this case in chalk country. Their origin is somewhat controversial and probably differs in different districts. They often complete the pattern of surface drainage, and springs are likely to emerge if and when the bottoms of these valleys reach a clay foundation, as in the area of Map 2 and Plate II where clay lies below the limestone plateau surface. These valleys thus give a clue to the geology. Sometimes old cottages are built in the sheltered bottoms of these dry valleys, as in Plate III.

Flood plains along the course of a large river give much scope for study. Records may be kept of the duration of floods, depth of water, drainage, and effects of possible floods on local communications. Natural vegetation, animal and bird life by the riverside and the use of alluvial land should be noted.

Coast erosion is complicated. The sculpture of cliffs by rain, frost and waves varies with the character of the rock. Compare the gravel cliffs in Plate X with the resistant igneous rocks of Plate VI. The highest peak in Plates V and VII shows how rocks of different hardness are affected by weathering. Soft sands are exposed at the top of the cliff, below is an exposure of sticky marl in which rain has worn vertical gullies, and below, again, are horizontal strata of harder sandstone, cut back at tide level, leaving detached rocks of this material. Coast erosion acts most rapidly during storms when waves can fling pebbles and sand against cliffs, and sea-water can enter crevices (Plate VI). These cracks may, later, be enlarged by frost or, in the case of limestone, by solution of the rock. Alternating hard and soft rocks reaching a coast form bays and headlands (Plate V). Chapter VII will refer to the formation of natural harbours, though many are now enlarged artificially. Submarine contours, as in Map 5, should be noted. Beach materials are also interesting, whether fragments from cliffs immediately behind, or brought from elsewhere by long-shore currents. Groins, when placed to check accumulation of shingle which might overwhelm the land or block a river-mouth, indicate the direction of these currents. Sand dunes occur on coasts of a different type, and in some districts steps are taken to prevent them spreading over the land.

Glaciation

Much "Earth Sculpture" was done during and after the period known as the "Great Ice Age" when, however, the climate altered in temperature many times. During the cooler periods, ice moved in many directions over this country, scraping the higher and harder rock-masses bare of soil, and in course of time glaciers which formed on the edge of the vast ice sheet (or on mountain masses when the main ice sheet began to shrink) modelled already existing valleys into characteristic shapes. Look at the valleys in Plate IV; find them in Map 3 and note their cross-sections compared with those in Map 2. The U-shape of the cross-sections is one of several clues as to whether valleys were once occupied by moving ice, and in some districts certain scratches on hard rock show the direction in which the ice moved. Such scratches can be seen on a low smooth rock close to the bridge south of Derwentwater (Map 3). Interesting as are such studies in themselves, however, the chief reason for studying glaciation in a local survey is to find out how it has affected human life in the past and present. A former glacier, for instance, by its weight, and with the materials embedded in it, hollowed out the basin in the valley bottom now filled by the lake. Moraines of mingled sand, clay, stones and rocks of different shapes and sizes are found on the valley sides and in some cases provide soil deep enough for trees. A moraine has been cut through for the road beyond this lake.

The widening of valley floors by old glaciers has meant that routes have been clearly defined in difficult country, and roads and, in some valleys, railways, run parallel with swift streams. So glaciation has indirectly caused villages and certain towns to grow up where such routes met, as in Plate IV and Map 3.

It is not only in wild mountain country that former glaciers have affected human life to-day. Some valleys in northern England and elsewhere have been so widened as to provide space for towns to spread along river banks on the materials spread by glacial action and the resulting floods. Such sites may become useful for seaports and shipbuilding, but in studying such a district it would be well to begin with a contour map of the physical features alone, and to make cross-sections of the valley where settlements have since grown up.

Now look at Plate IX (page 50)—very different country from that in Plate IV (page 20), but also affected by the "Great Ice Age," though it is a lowland district. It is not always realized that the Great Ice Age left results on lowlands, which, though less spectacular than those in hill country, may be even more important for man. When the climate gradually became intermittently and then permanently warmer and vast floods overwhelmed the country, material which had been carried on the ice, or embedded in it, or scraped up from below, was spread in sheets over the lower ground. This is known in general as Glacial Drift or named on some geological maps as Pleistocene Deposits. It may be heaped-up gravel or sand, or Boulder Clay which, containing a mixture of rock fragments from many sources, forms a sticky soil where ice once covered the land. These drifts are not yet completely mapped so here is scope for useful work by the more experienced members of a local survey. These soils can be recognized by the variety of stones in them, and pebbles in them may even show scratches by ice.

These drifts, where found, should be plotted on the 6 in. map. Boulder clay or Pleistocene gravel may form undulations in what would otherwise be flat country, altering the surface soil (for better or worse) and so affecting agriculture. Drift also provided sites for settlements on what otherwise would have been swampy land in the days before modern drainage.

Plate IX (page 50) gives an impression of a glaciated lowland.

The relief is due to the unequal thickness of the drift. Compare the height of the hill in this picture (735 feet) with that of the peaks in Plate IV, which rise to over 2000 feet, and are made of hard slates (metamorphic rock). The small, rounded, morainic hills in Plate IX are of sands and gravels with beds of clay, and the soil, unlike that on the uplands in Plate IV, is deep enough for trees and hedgerows, though the bent-over trees suggest strong wind.

On the lowland area of Plate I and Map 2 are patches of post-glacial gravel brought down by the floods which naturally followed the Great Ice Age; these add interest to the district in various ways. Besides determining the sites of many villages and farms, these gravels may contain relics of pre-history. For very early man, contemporary with mammoths and other strange creatures now extinct, such as the woolly rhinoceros, lived near the border of the ice-covered region, during the periods when the climate became temporarily warmer. So the tools of these people, along with bones, tusks and teeth of the huge animals that they hunted, may be found in the gravels spread by floods from melting ice.

Drifts, therefore, dating from the Ice Age or following it, should always be taken into account in problems of human geography in lowland districts in the north and midlands of England, where villages are often seen slightly raised above the general level of the country. Former glaciation has also given rise to or developed certain human activities. For instance in mountain districts the waterfalls which are found on the steep sides of U-shaped valleys may be used to generate power, while geology, modified by ice-action in the past, gives us the magnificent scenery enjoyed by visitors as well as residents and so has brought about a tourist industry. In lowland country, gravel pits are worked, and ponds may be made in boulder clay. Plant-life, and agriculture too, is influenced by the mixed soils in drifts.

SOME PROBLEMS AND EXPERIMENTS

(Questions 1–4 are the most suitable for beginners and younger students)

1. Is the foundation rock of your district exposed in sea-cliffs, quarries, railway cuttings, or foundations of houses? Note and record its colour, texture (whether hard and smooth, or gravelly, sandy, or sticky), and

whether it is divided by joints or shows definite strata. In which direction and how steeply do the strata dip or tilt, and are they bent or folded? Make drawings or take photographs of any good exposures and plot their positions on your map.

2. Describe any mineral veins, interesting crystals, or fossils you may find, and have them correctly named by a geologist or at a museum. Record where these specimens were found and if on the surface or if below, and at what depth.

3. Find out how and where your local rocks are used.

4. Note, in your district, the shapes of hills and valleys, and the relative steepness of slopes formed by various rocks. If more than one type of scenery occurs near you, are the differences due to the rocks?

5. If you live near the sea, find out if the cliffs are hard and rocky (dangerous for ships), or soft and easily worn back. Is the sea encroaching on the land and at what rate? Map any landslips, sand dunes, or other coastal features not conspicuous on the local maps.

6. How much are sites of towns in your district influenced by the geology? Are they sited or shaped by areas liable to flood, bogs, or presence or absence of water-supply? Try to map the shape and extent of old villages or towns before these were changed by modern building development.

7. Find out if springs in your district are permanent or seasonal, and map them accordingly. Try to discover the depth at which water occurs in wells and record it for different seasons.

8. Map any dry valleys, indicating where they become deeper or narrower. Mark and note details of topography where they join a stream.

9. Note any land-forms which affect human beings. Draw cross-sections of valleys which are used for communications.

10. If there are caves near you, describe the rocks in which they occur. If you can find any accounts of the extent and depth of the caves, mark these on your map.

11. Note, and if possible photograph and map, any destruction by landslide, flood, or falling cliffs.

12. Describe and map any place where man has modified scenery by damming rivers, or flooding valleys, draining swamps, blasting rock for roads, making railway-cuttings, artificial harbours, mines, and slag-heaps.

13. If possible, find out approximate depth of any lake, pond, or reservoir.

CHAPTER V

APPROACH THROUGH STUDY OF AGRICULTURE

AGRICULTURE is one of the most obvious methods of approach to the study of a rural district and observations are within the capabilities of some of the younger scholars, though linked up with many complicated problems to be considered later.

First Impressions

Look again at Plates I, IV and IX (pages 12, 20 and 50). What impressions do they give of farming in each of these localities?

In Plate IX cattle graze in a meadow bordering water which, like that in Plate I, is a reservoir (a dammed up stream in this case), not a deep rock basin, like the lake in Plate IV. Glacial drift has produced the soil in Plate IX (sands and gravel with beds of clay), with its long grass in the waterside meadow, but, where the land rises beyond it, crops are grown (oats, mangolds, and hay). A wood, containing pines, oak, silver birch, holly and sycamore covers part of the hillside, while the summit is used for a public park crowned with a war memorial. There are no sheep in this area—in contrast to the flocks of Herdwick sheep which occupy the fells of Plate IV (cattle are kept in some of the water meadows near the lake here) and the mixed farms of arable, grazing land, and small orchards on the lower slopes of the scarp in Plate I. Field boundaries are of different material in these districts also.

Mapping the Uses of Land

To make a satisfactory record of what you see of the farming in your own district, you will need a 6 in. map, which shows the boundary of every field, as Map 1. It is quite a simple matter to walk about the country and mark on the map which fields are used for grass and which are arable and afterwards to colour them accordingly. Care should be taken to distinguish "permanent" from "temporary" grass-land, which beginners sometimes find puzzling. The latter is, of course, included in a rotation of crops.

The rotation of crops in your district can be found if a series of land utilization maps is made, covering at least four years. The reasons for growing certain special crops peculiar to one or several localities, such as hops, sugar beet, mustard, flower bulbs, flax, must be found by inquiry, and records of any crops which have been grown in the past and are no longer grown in the district should be looked for.

The dates of the sowing and harvesting of each crop would be of interest and could be written in the appropriate field. These dates could be compared with weather records for the current year. The aspect of the field, especially if on sloping ground, and in consequence the amount of sunshine, is important in this connexion. Dates of late frost and the duration of snow-drifts might also be added to the map.

Movements of stock throughout the year could be plotted on the 6 in. map, with dates of such events as lambing and sheep shearing. Times of daily milking and of feeding animals throughout the year might be noted.

Fruit growing is a study in itself, and of great importance in many districts. Note the positions of orchards in Map 1 (page 16), sheltered from the south-west winds on the good mixed soils washed down from the scarp where geological boundaries are found. In Plate V and Map 5, we have seen how horizontal geological formations are cut short and exposed in the cliffs. Naturally they crop out at about the same levels on valley sides. The lower slopes are the most fertile here, as in Plate I. Again, dates for the ripening and gathering of fruit each year can be related to weather records. There is scope for research on what soil fruit trees seem to flourish best, and on the pests which destroy the fruit.

Poultry and pigs are plentiful in some districts. Under what conditions are they kept, and where are they marketed and what use is made of them? Plants commonly known as *weeds* must not be forgotten in a study of agricultural land of any kind. The following have been noted in the area of Plate IX, on the varied Glacial Drifts. Here, on sandy bank were found red spurrey, sheep's sorrel, field thistle, knot grass, poppies and hawkweed. On loamy soils were nettle, sow thistle, pimpernel, charlock, chickweed and ox-eye daisy. On patches of bog and heavy clay were rest-harrow, wild carrot, cotton

MAP 5. PART OF THE DEVONSHIRE COAST: 1 IN. TO 1 MILE

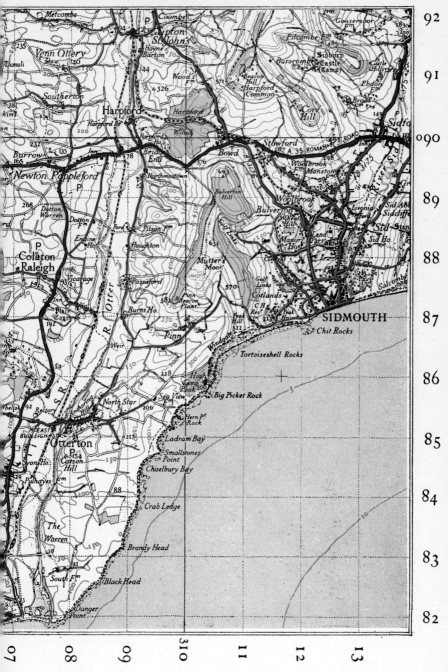

MAP 6. DOVER HARBOUR: $2\frac{1}{2}$ IN. TO I MILE (APPROX.)

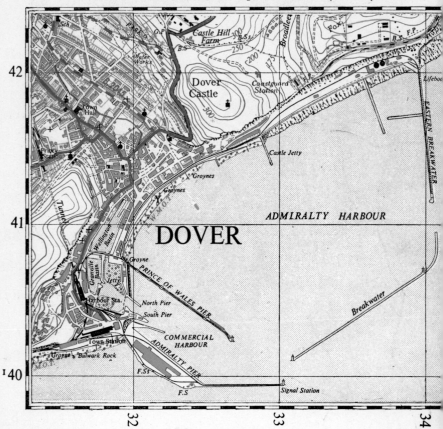

grass, bog-rush, mare's-tail and primrose. In studying vegetation in a local survey, it is more useful to record on the map sites where certain typical plants flourish and are plentiful rather than finds of rare plants, though these should be noted and carefully preserved. For instance, the common plants in the areas of Plates I, II and IV would be very different.

Field boundaries (stone walls, ditches with or without water, banks of earth, wire fences and hurdles should be distinguished on the map, stone where it is abundant and soil thin (Plate III), hedges where soil can support trees (Plate I) and where stone is not available (Plate IX). Ditches are often used for draining marshy land, wire fences may be found dividing a field shown on the map as one, or old divisions may have been removed. Additions and new boundaries should be inserted. Hurdles are often used for folding sheep and therefore are not permanent.

Ancient Crafts

A school in an Oxfordshire village discovered that hurdle-making had been carried on there in one family for nearly 300 years, and the craft of "dry walling" as practised to-day in the Cotswolds is in direct descent from the stone walls found in the "barrows" or tombs of the men of the "New Stone Age" built about 4000 years ago; the thatching of roofs and of stacks is bound up with agricultural traditions. Hedges need skilled work too, and it may be observed how the branches are inter-laced and the plants used to the best advantage, also the methods of pruning. Interesting *study of wild life* can be carried on in the careful examination of a hedge, especially if it is bordered by a ditch or is set on an earth bank, and here is an opportunity to encourage children to respect and take care of the wild life they see, to spare the rare plants and above all the birds and their nests and eggs, and for them to learn which birds are useful to gardens and farms, and what insect pests they eat. Many samples of the wild life of England can be found also in ditches and in stone walls. The latter often harbour snakes which come out in hot weather, and children may well learn to distinguish poisonous adders from those which are harmless, perhaps by seeing specimens in museums and drawing them. Berries or fungi which are poisonous should be noted and drawings made of them.

Preservation of Game

The study of wild life naturally leads on to the problem of *game* and its destruction and preservation, about which there is much difference of opinion and need for careful thought. Try to discover from books or inquiry which creatures are definitely harmful to the farming industry. Any observations, by those making the local survey, of foxes, badgers, otters or hares should be noted and the time and place recorded. Scholars should be able to describe methods of hunting these, and their traditions in the district, and here is a chance to encourage the humane treatment of wild creatures. *Fishing* also has its local customs and traditions, whether in sea or river, and here is another hobby which would be of use if included in a local survey. Perhaps the study of *Forestry* is taking us rather far from our studies of farming, but agricultural land is often varied with woods and coppices and here again is scope for the study of vegetation, its relation to local soil and climate and its economic uses. Woodland should be observed throughout the year; the influence of the shade of trees on undergrowth is an important point to study.

Soil

Though agricultural land is much modified by artificial fertilizers, soil is directly connected with its geological background as described in the last chapter, for it is the weathered, decomposed and broken-up surface of the rock foundation. Notice in Plate IV the difference in the utilization of the land between the mountain slopes where soil is thin or absent and the soft alluvial area on the lowland near the lake; it should be remembered, however, that soft deep soil is not always fertile. Breaking up of soil may be caused by action of frost, burrowing animals, earthworms, or the roots of plants. The mineral contents of the soil, whether in lime, sand, clay, granite, slate, etc., are important, of course, and scholars will naturally take note of the colour of the soil.

Climate

This is obviously important in an agricultural district. Some crops need more sunshine than others do, and these do not flourish in western England where rainfall is heavy. Some cannot stand intense cold; others need plenty of moisture at certain seasons. When the most flourishing crops in the district have been noted, it is interesting to compare figures for temperature and rainfall with those of another district where the most successful crops are different. Results of observations at three stations within a few miles of each other on Map 2 show that the first, on a valley-side about 600 feet higher than the second, receives more rain during most of the year, except in late summer when it escapes many of the thunderstorms that follow the broad low flood plain containing the second station. The third station receives rain from the south-west winds rising over the scarp behind it.

Another important aspect of local climate is "inversion of temperature" often occurring in deep valleys where cold, heavy air sinks at night, making valley bottoms colder than the slopes above. This often occurs in the valley in Plate II, for instance, and causes frosts in spring, disastrous for orchards planted on the lower slopes or in the bottom of such valleys. These frosts, their positions and dates, and the altitude below which the frost occurred, might well be recorded in the agricultural map for the year.

Boundaries of river floods with date of observation and height of flood water would be interesting records for future use, especially if correlated with rainfall figures.

Sites and Sizes of Farms

Boundaries of farm lands can be drawn on the 6 in. map, including "rough pasture," "water-meadows" or woodland. It is good practice for scholars to calculate the acreage of fields here shown, and to study the layout of the farm buildings, and the materials of which they are built, and whether existing buildings have replaced older ones.

Parish Boundaries

The size and shape of the parish is often, rather unexpectedly, connected with types of soil within it. A parish often grew out on an ancient manor or more than one, and a manor usually included within it arable land, water-meadows, a mill, and a certain amount of "waste" which was either woodland or rough pasture. Therefore most parishes will, on examination, be found to include at least two distinct geological formations (even if one of these is "drift" not marked on a small scale geological map) and these give rise to differences in the natural background. This is evident when parish boundaries are traced and placed over a geological map. The tracings can be made from the Index Sheets published by the Ordnance Survey for each county (which show parishes and the site of the church in each) and placed over geological maps on the same scale, $\frac{1}{4}$ in. to 1 mile.

Parish boundaries are interesting in themselves, and those shown on the 6 in. map should be followed as far as possible, *on foot*, and studied carefully. They often follow physical features, such as streams or water-partings, or sometimes a very ancient road or trackway, which is thus shown to be older than the parish.

Increase or decrease in the population of a parish is found by comparing census returns (which can often be found in a public library) during the last hundred years or so, and graphs made from them may be very striking if related to events in local history. Such studies should not be merely on paper, but should be carried on side by side with observations of any new houses which may have been built and of the sites of any which have disappeared, since the local map was surveyed.

This leads on to other aspects of local history, and in a rural district this might begin with the collecting and recording of old field names. These might be found by inquiry from farmers or old inhabitants of the district, or, where these names are being forgotten, by consulting the Tithe Maps of the parish, which in many cases were compiled about a hundred years ago. The names sometimes refer to some peculiarity of the physical background or to the name (often much altered) of a former owner, or to some local legend or tradition (such as the name "Puck's Close" of a field known to the author, of which the reason seems to be forgotten). But though the origins of such names are in many cases hard to discover and so give rise to rather wild guesses, the placing of these in the respective fields on the 6 in. map occasionally helps to solve a problem.

Existing foot-paths are marked on the 6 in. maps but are

PLATE VI. IGNEOUS ROCKS IN CORNWALL

PLATE VII. GEOLOGICAL EXPOSURES IN SOUTH DEVON COAST

42

PLATE VIII. PART OF AN INDUSTRIAL TOWN

not always "Rights of Way." These should be discovered, recorded, and *used* from time to time, to keep them open. It is also interesting and useful to record what rights or privileges local people have with regard to the uses of commons or woodlands. "Trespassing" on private property without permission should be forbidden; such permission would very likely be given if the object of the "exploration" was explained by the students.

Local Industries

Local industries, whether still active, extinct, or in abeyance, should be noted, when, and why, any ceased to function, and whether any new activities have come to the district in recent years. If so, how have these affected village life? It is worth while, too, to record before they are forgotten any old customs of interest, local cookery recipes, legends, old songs, and sports. And, in addition to the festivals of the Church, how far do scholars realize the significance of, say, Harvest Festivals, Guy Fawkes' Day, May Day, Boxing Day, and perhaps additional anniversaries peculiar to the district? And of course they should watch and note changes in methods of farming, and the introduction and use of various kinds of agricultural machinery. For those interested in history there is scope for the study of these, in comparison with early methods of farming, even going back to the beginnings of agriculture and the domestication of animals in Neolithic times about 4000 years ago and to the medieval systems of farming. Old agricultural implements, some used within living memory, can be seen in many museums. Old farm wagons differ much in different districts and have long traditions.

Markets

Having discovered what the farmers of the district produce, we are next led to find out what becomes of the produce, whether it is eaten or used by the producers and their neighbours, or sent elsewhere. A map on the scale of 1 in. to the mile, or even on a smaller scale showing a larger area, is useful in showing the markets to which produce goes. The distances should be worked out, together with descriptions of the means of transport used to-day and in the past, and the time taken in these journeys—if by road, whether by horse or motor transport, or, for long distances, whether by rail, canal, or lorry. Milk, vegetables, poultry and fruit may go to the nearest town; particulars of milk rounds might be noted and mapped. On the other hand, specialized products such as apples for cider, hops for beer, and "luxury" vegetables may go farther afield. It cannot be emphasized too much how economic conditions are changing and that those of yesterday do not hold good to-day. These changes should be watched. The distribution of meat and wool may lead to inquiries about London and other distant markets and sea-ports—a vast subject! It will often be found that transport under modern conditions has led to smaller markets growing less important or disappearing in favour of larger ones further away. Crops have many destinations, whether as human or animal food.

There is work to be done, too, in observing and recording the increasing movements of people between town and country, whether for business, shopping or amusement, and also the results of the former isolation of villages being thus broken down. Useful discussions with older scholars may arise as to how far this is to the advantage of town or country, or to both or neither; the changes brought about, in a rural district, by the coming of the railway (about a hundred years ago), by the developments in cycling and motor traffic (about forty years ago), and by the increasing "tourist industry" to-day should not be forgotten.

Although this chapter has dealt with topics which mainly apply to a rural district, a survey from a town centre may well consider some of them. Many large towns contain the sites of old farms, and street names such as "Sheep Street" or "Green Lane" (the latter occurs in London)! may suggest rural life in the past. Market gardens, if not farms, are often found close to or in towns or suburbs, and weeds grow even in such districts as that in Plate VIII. The wild flowers which have so quickly spread over bombed areas are full of interest. The shapes, sizes, and boundaries of urban as well as rural parishes may well be related to a geological map as suggested above, and farm produce can be studied from the point of view of the market and the shops! But in a survey of an urban district it is probably best to *begin* by a different method of approach.

SOME PROBLEMS AND EXPERIMENTS

(Questions 1–6 and 17 are the most suitable for beginners and younger students)

1. Mark on the 6-in. map of your district, fields which are arable or under grass. Mark orchards, marshes, commons, and building land. What crops are grown, and what numbers and kinds of animals are in each field throughout the year? Compare such maps for different years and note the rotation of crops.

2. What fruit is grown in the orchards near you and where, and for what is it used? Record dates of pruning and gathering fruit, and compare with your weather records.

3. Note where pigs and poultry are kept. Where, and to whom, and for what purpose are they sold?

4. Make drawings of any cultivated plants peculiar to or characteristic of your district. Describe methods of cultivation.

5. Map different kinds of field boundaries. How are they made?

6. Make lists of plants found in hedgerows, and weeds in cultivated fields, with dates of flowering. (Do not gather rare plants.) Make lists and drawings of birds, but do not touch nests or eggs. Find out what the birds eat and how they benefit gardens.

7. Draw pictures of fungi and berries which are poisonous.

8. If there is woodland in your district, make a list of trees and plants in the undergrowth. For what are the trees used, and where?

9. Compare soils in different parts of your district, their colour, texture, and depth. What plants grow best in each type of soil?

10. Record temperature, rainfall, and direction of wind throughout the year at the same time each day, and if possible compare them with those at a different height above sea-level. From what direction does the wind most often blow? Note local climate depending on aspect of slope, shelter from wind, or "inversion of temperature." Study the daily weather forecasts and compare them with your own observations.

11. Map the extent of river floods, and compare with rainfall figures. Note and measure depths of snowdrifts, and record dates of snowfall and thaw. Note duration of drifts on slopes of different aspects.

12. Watch methods of farming and any uses of agricultural machines. Compare new with old methods. Look for specimens of old-fashioned farm implements in a museum.

13. Find out boundaries of farms and acreage of fields. If possible, compare with those elsewhere. Find out by inquiry at farms or from "tithe maps" the old names of the fields and mark them on your 6-in. map.

14. Find out and mark on a 6-in. map the earliest dates of the church or chapel, school, inn, forge, or carpenter's shop (if any), village hall, cinema, police station, surgery, and railway station (if any) in your village. Sketch them.

15. Find out markets to which local farm produce is sent. Measure, on the map, distance by road or rail.

16. Find the boundaries of your parish and try to walk along them.

Do they follow any physical features? Note the position of parish church within them. Is there more than one type of country within the parish?

17. Make a list of the festivals and holidays observed throughout the year. Why are they observed?

18. Collect any special cookery recipes peculiar to the district. Describe any local games or sports, with long traditions.

CHAPTER VI

APPROACH THROUGH STUDY OF ROUTES BY ROAD AND RIVER

MANY of those who want to start a local survey may find themselves near a meeting place of routes, roads, canals, railways—or possibly all of these, with a town or village which has grown up through being at a route centre.

Important communications in any particular region may often be traced back into early history, although routes, and also means of transport along them are still being modified and changed, often by reason of circumstances outside the immediate locality. But geographical background has always counted and still does, either directly or indirectly.

Geographical Background to Communications

Map 3 (page 25) and Plate IV (page 20) show a clear example of physical control over routes in mountain country. Roads have to follow valleys, which, in north England as in Scotland and Wales, have been conveniently enlarged and widened by glaciers of long ago. These valleys thus enable a road, and in some cases a railway, to run parallel with the stream below, although, even so, the valley may have to be artificially widened in places. At the junction of such valleys small towns naturally grew up, so dependent on their setting that a study of such centres soon leads to considerations of local geology. Note, in Plate IV and Map 3, the U-shaped valleys leading down to the lake. Each is followed by a trackway or road. A town such as that in Plate IV, having dealt in the past with products of the surrounding hill-country brought to it by valley routes, has now developed an important tourist industry due to the magnificent surrounding scenery, and it is significant that the most important building in Plate IV is a hotel! The tourist industry in its turn has led to the widening and straightening of many local roads. The railway, important as being the only one in a large area, and prominent on the map, is less conspicuous in the photograph, but can be traced in the foreground

47

of the picture. It is not only in mountain country that physical features may make communications difficult. Railway tunnels are necessary in approaches to the town in Map 6. Flood plains may be quite as awkward as hills. Note the comparatively empty north-west corner of Map 1 (page 16). The very varied types of route leading to the large city, especially where they descend from uplands to vale are much influenced by physical geography. The "gap" in Plate II has been discussed in a previous chapter.

Towns on Routes Determined by Distant Conditions

In some cases settlements grew up at the meetings and crosings of routes whose importance lay outside the immediate area. Such a town was the Roman "Corinium" (Cirencester) which in the first century A.D. developed at the crossing place of several of the great military roads, and such is Crewe which in the nineteenth century developed where railways met from London, N.W. England and Scotland, and from N. Wales.

When studying such towns, small-scale maps covering a large area are needed, to give some idea of the destinations and purposes of the routes to and from them. Their history should be considered, and the needs of the people who used them in the past might be compared with those of to-day. The changes continually taking place in traffic along old roads should be noted and recorded from personal observation; these might include an increase in numbers of cars, lorries, motor coaches or cycles, or the abandonment of an old road in favour of a more direct route. The influence of physical geography on these routes may be great in any one area, or it may be more important further afield.

We have already seen how much agriculture depends on markets and in rural districts it is very common to find roads from all directions leading to a town which has for long been a market and shopping centre for the district (as Plate IV). Gloucester (see Map 1) has been such a centre for a very long period, being moreover at the lowest crossing place, by road, of the River Severn. The "gap" in Plate IV where several routes converge is used by one old road leading down the steep escarpment to the "port" of Gloucester and is accordingly called the "Portway."

A local survey might begin with the study of a market, what is sold there, how the market is reached, and how far its approaches were determined by physical geography, also whether the goods sold in the market to-day differ much from those sold in the past.

Gap Towns

Roads and trackways meet near many a gap through a line or group of hills, and in some cases a railway, too, passes through it. A village or market town would naturally grow up near a gap, such as those in the North and South Downs. A gap in the Cotswolds, with Stroud at its mouth, is used by a road, a canal (now disused) and a railway running close to a stream. This "gap" however is blocked at one end by hill country over which the road climbs, while tunnels take the railway and old canal through it. Such different communications naturally need careful study of the physical features which control their respective routes.

Settlements at River Crossings

Most of our large cities of any considerable age and also many smaller country towns are situated on a river—wide or narrow, swift or sluggish as the case may be—and we find that most of these towns are entered by roads from many directions, as in Map 2. If a survey in such area is being attempted we might begin by looking first at its importance as a route centre even though at first sight other aspects of it may seem more striking. It is important to remember that transport by water was more important in the past than it is to-day. Therefore such a survey should begin with some first-hand observations of the river itself, noting up to what point it is, or was, navigable, at high and low tide respectively, what boats can, or could, use it and why the river is crossed at *that particular place*. When studying such a bridge-town you will need to know something of the source and destination of the river and of the kind of country through which it flows both above and below the area of your survey. You should, therefore, look at a small-scale map which shows most, or all, of the river's course. The swiftness and power of the current is affected by its volume and by the gradient of the river-bed, so it should be noted whether the stream rises in high mountain country (like the River Severn) or on low ground like the head-stream of the Thames. For example, in a comparison of the sites of Gloucester and Oxford (both on important river crossings) we find that if these two cities were equally near the source of its river the current at Gloucester would be much swifter than that at Oxford, as the source of the river is on higher ground, but this is modified by the fact that the source of the Severn is at a greater distance and that the river flows over much low flat country before it reaches Gloucester.

Flood Plains

Many rivers such as these have developed wide, swinging meanders through meadows which are liable to floods after rain. These are not always in the lower part of the river as one might expect. It is important to know to what extent these meadows are being artificially drained and how soon, after the floods have disappeared, they can be put to practical use. Also how much above normal flood level the different parts of a city were built at different periods of its history, and to what extent the likelihood of floods hampers its growth.

Tidal Estuaries

A further comparison between the sites of Gloucester and Oxford shows that Gloucester is sufficiently near to the mouth of its river (where this widens into an estuary) to be affected by tides, as Oxford is not. The celebrated "bore" which flows up the Severn at certain seasons depends on the shape of the estuary and the direction of the incoming tide, and wind. The Severn is not the only river where a tidal wave is seen. There is much scope in a local survey centred on an estuary for observations of tides, their heights at different seasons and their effects on shipping.

When a general idea of the river as a whole has been gained from maps and all water-courses in the immediate area have been traced from the 6 in. map, the nearest river-crossing should be looked at with great care and observations made on the character of the river-banks and bottom there. Note should be made as to whether the soil is firm gravel or sticky clay; whether there was a ford there before the bridge was built, and

PLATE IX. A DISTRICT OF GLACIAL DRIFT

PLATE X. GRAVEL CLIFFS IN SUFFOLK

PLATE XI. WELLINGTON DOCK, DOVER

PLATE XII. DOVER FROM THE AIR

51

by whom it was used; and whether old maps or records show if the original ford was on the site of the present crossing or at a place where the river was either narrower, shallower, or had a firmer bottom than could be found either up or downstream. As an example the original Severn crossing seems to have been upstream from the present bridge at Gloucester (Map 2) and was used by the Romans who made a camp and afterwards built a town where there military road crossed the Severn into South Wales. The course of this road was made easier across the swampy vale of the Severn because it could use patches of post-glacial gravel, the interesting origin of which was mentioned in Chapter IV. In these gravels (spread in places over the low-lying clay lands) tools of very early prehistoric people and remains of extinct animals (such as the mammoth) have been found. The ancient city of Gloucester stands slightly above flood level where these gravels most nearly approach the river. The opposite side of the Severn is lower, often flooded, and still empty of buildings.

Wild Life and Nature Study on River Banks

Open spaces of this kind give good opportunities for the study of wild life. On the Severn banks is the land used by a "Wild Fowl Trust" where much research on bird-life is being done. On many river banks nature can be studied less formally, and plants specially characteristic of the district (such as the famous fritillaries of the Oxford meadows) should be treasured. Common plants should be listed and accounted for, and it should be the aim of every survey group that the rarer ones be protected and saved from extinction.

The Thames ford at Oxford became important rather later than that across the Severn. The river was crossed on the border between two Saxon kingdoms, where the land was very swampy and broken by many waterways. We are told that most of the old roads were brought to the city on causeways, but a road from the south (perhaps the oldest), meeting another from the east, here found on the north bank of the river a strip of firm gravel between the Thames and the Cherwell, along which the town of Oxford spread and is still spreading.

Such conditions can be found in connexion with many riverside towns, and help to explain the extent and direction of their growth. The gathering together of roads at such points, moreover, often leads, as in the case of the two cities mentioned above (or where routes converge on a lake as in Map 3 and Plate IV) to the development of old and noted markets. Produce sold in such markets largely depended in the past on the products of the country from which the roads come, as well as on local industries. This is less marked now in consequence of developments in communications.

River Ports

Trade is of course increased where the river is large enough for a port. With the increase in size of ships many old ports have been partially replaced by newer ones farther down the river, and although in the past river transport was sometimes the only means of communication between one region and another, as ships grew larger the rivers were used less. Many are shallow with submerged and shifting sandbanks; tides in the estuaries call for skilled navigation and wide meanders in flat country wasted much time. Hence we often find straight canals built beside the winding rivers to ensure deep enough water for barges. The dates of such canals, as well as the goods they carry, should be noted. Referring to Map 2, ocean-going ships come into a port down the Severn estuary, south-west of this map, and from there goods are sent up to Gloucester, either by road or by the canal parallel to the lower Severn. Small boats and barges come to Gloucester still. Our other example of a bridge-town, Oxford, builds boats, but its river-traffic is mainly for recreation, though a canal brings goods from the north. A comparison of the importance of canal and river transport, and the routes followed by both, can in many districts also be related to that by road and rail. Positions of locks on canals, toll houses (past and still existing) on the roads, level crossings, tunnels, and viaducts can well be studied in connexion with the physical features of the district.

Uses of Roads Past and Present

Roads leading to river crossings have had many uses throughout history. For instance, to Gloucester they brought Roman armies, pilgrims to the Cathedral, farmers and traders (to markets and fairs) from the west of England and from Wales, timber and grain from the docks at Sharpness, iron and coal from the Forest of Dean. To Oxford came pilgrims and visitors to the great Abbeys, friars and students from all parts of the country, even from Europe. Both towns received stage coaches from London, and now to both centres come materials for modern industry, workers to the factories, country house-wives for shopping and the cinema, and innumerable tourists.

A town tends to grow outwards along these converging roads, which thus largely determine its modern shape, and the spread of towns which has taken place since the last revision of the local map should be carefully noted and recorded.

Railway Stations

Approaches to towns by railways are often determined by local geography. Map 6 shows that tunnels are sometimes needed. The positions of railway stations (early or mid-nineteenth-century additions to the town) are sometimes inter-esting. Owing to a good deal of early prejudice against rail-ways on the part of the townspeople, stations were often built well outside the existing towns, which have since grown out to reach them by streets of ugly nineteenth-century houses.

Sea ports have grown up at route junctions of rather a differ-ent kind, where communications by land and sea converge. They too are largely controlled by geographical conditions, either local or far away. We will therefore next consider some special problems to be dealt with in a local survey near the coast.

SOME PROBLEMS AND EXPERIMENTS

(Exercises 3 and 6 and 9 are suitable for beginners and younger students)

1. In exploring mountain country, make detailed observations of a valley where a road and a railway follow the course of a stream. Note where these separate, and where the valley has been artificially widened.

2. Make a map of any junction of long-distance routes which meet in your district, indicating whence they come. Describe their uses in past and present. Note how natural features may have influenced the courses of these routes.

3. If your market is approached from many directions, note the produce brought from each, and whence customers come to market. What do these facts tell you of the farm life of the district?

4. If you are near a natural "gap" or "pass," note the surrounding

physical features and the formation and probable causes of the gap itself. Describe any use made of it in recent years.

5. Look at the river-banks and river-bed near any bridge. Make a small-scale map of the river from source to mouth. Find out the date of the bridge and if it has replaced an earlier bridge or a ford.

6. Study any areas liable to flood, and observe the wild life on the open spaces of the flood plain. Has this been drained in recent years or long ago? How has this probably affected (a) wild life, (b) the growth of a town or suburbs?

7. How far upstream and to what extent do tides affect river navigation in your district?

8. Study the courses of any canals or railways which come to your survey area or near it. Has the importance of these routes increased or decreased in recent years? Where do canal locks occur and why?

9. Note the position of the railway station. Was it built inside the town or is the town spreading towards it?

CHAPTER VII

LOCAL SURVEYS BY THE SEA

COASTAL surveys, on a large scale, can be made intensively only by a limited number of schools or survey groups, and in these special problems arise. But other groups can profitably make less detailed references to coastal geography, for instance by studying a 1 in. map, as Map 5 (page 38), with the corresponding photograph (Plate V, page 21). Such references may help to widen the knowledge even of those making surveys inland. Many scholars, moreover, see parts of the coast when on holiday, and often find satisfaction in references afterwards to places that they have known and enjoyed.

We have already noted that among the many problems connected with human activities and natural conditions are lines of route and route junctions. Also we have already discussed the advantage to a survey if the area contains contrasting or varied types of country. A sea coast separating sea and land gives us the greatest contrast to be found in any area. And just as settlements grew up where land-routes met, often on the boundary between two "natural regions," so seaports (large or small) developed where land- and sea-routes met.

We should try to understand the physical background in order to explain the reason for any town or village site, and therefore students near the sea should examine the type of coast in the district. Does it most resemble Plates V, VI or X, or none of these? The scenery in each of these pictures depends on the rocks and their geological history. Moreover sea-cliffs are merely the cut-off ends of geological formations inland, so such ready-made geological sections are very useful in a general investigation of the district. For instance the succession and arrangement of the rocks exposed in Plates V and VII, continued inland, are important in local agriculture. Land-forms and all that is influenced by them would obviously be very different where the foundation rock is similar to that of Plates VI or X.

Plate VI (page 42) suggests hard rocks exposed to violent

storms and heavy seas. It so happens that in Britain the coasts facing the Atlantic are mainly made of resistant igneous rock where marine erosion works along joints, some of which may ultimately be enlarged into caves. Lines of weakness, sometimes due to "faulting," may cause narrow inlets on a larger scale. Joints in the rock, as in Plate VI, may separate some of the more resistant masses from the cliffs behind, to form small islands or "stacks." Others can be seen in Plate VII, although the rock here is not so hard as that in Plate VI.

Erosion on such a coast naturally produces a very irregular and often dangerous coastline, with inlets most of which can harbour only small boats.

It happens that in Britain the most violent storms blow from the south-west and so affect coasts such as these, and most of the work is done during storms when the force of the waves is supplemented by rock fragments hurled against the cliffs. In some districts the land has sunk in late geological times, thus increasing the irregular outline of such a coast as that in Plate VI and the submarine contours (shown on 1 in. maps in fathoms) are likely to show deep water near a steep and rugged shore. Plates VI and VII show that the cutting back of rocks is most active between high and low tide level. Rock falls from above and is removed by the tides. The shore-line platform so made may, or may not, be covered by rock fragments or heaped up shingle known as "the beach," or such fallen fragments may be carried along the coast by tides or currents and even may block, or partly block, and turn aside mouths of rivers which have not enough force to keep a channel open. Drifts of shingle are often restrained and regulated by groins along much of the south coast, where the beach is carried eastwards, while on most of the east coast it is carried southwards. This is indicated in Plate X (page 50), which shows a very different type of coast from that in Plate VI. Here the low cliffs are of a much more recent geological formation; some of the sands and gravels to be found in East Anglia are very soft and in many places cliffs are being washed away so frequently that changes can be watched and recorded from year to year. Buildings on this coast are in danger in times of storms—Plate X shows an attempt to prevent further encroachment by the sea. The coast-line in Plate X would be less indented than that in

Plate VI, and submarine contours near such a shore are likely to indicate more shallow water. Beach materials, too, would be different. The sand heaped up on the shore below the cliffs, as in Plate X, hides any undercutting at tide level. Such sand may contain a variety of pebbles where glacial drift occurs in the cliffs above. The height of such a cliff should be noted in comparison with that of the houses, and the thickness of various exposures of gravel measured. These cliffs should be compared with those of other districts known to the students and seen on other 1 in. maps

There are landslips sometimes after heavy rain where porous rock occurs above impervious clay or marl and gets waterlogged. These should give scope for mapping and observing new conditions, and old maps of the coast during historic times, if available, are interesting to compare with those of to-day. Plants on or near the shore should be observed and listed and drawings made of the most common and characteristic ones. These are often very profuse on a landslip with its mixed soil.

Plate V (page 21) shows a type of coast intermediate between those of Plates VI and X. Here are horizontal exposures of rocks of differing resistance (and of colour, when seen in the field). The picture shows some detached rocks and wide shallow bays.

Not all coasts have sea-cliffs. Others known to the survey group may have low shores or be bordered by sand-dunes, which have their own special problems of land-forms and vegetation.

We can now try to apply some general principles of coast formation to details seen in a landscape, or, failing that, in a photograph. Map 5 and Plate V represent a coast which is at first sight less exciting than one of the indented coasts of igneous rock, or than a flat salt-marsh or sand-dune coast with its very distinctive vegetation, but the series of horizontal strata shown in Plate V make it, perhaps, more complicated, and the varied colours of the rocks, as seen in the field, are more striking than their form. What is the effect of these strata on the country inland? They are seen in detail in Plate VII and are the cut-off ends of long, narrow, flat-topped ridges capped with the formation shown on the summit of the cliff, bare of houses and with few trees, though the steep valley-sides are often clothed with woodland above more fertile rock below. If the scenery in the picture is compared with Map 5 it will be seen how the contours are cut off where the cliffs are high and steep, and where these ridges end.

The photographer (Plate V) stood on the extreme east of the map, looking over the little steep-sided wooded valley reaching the sea, Plate V shows "Chit Rocks" exposed to view, evidently at low tide. In a local survey the range of high and low tide might be measured against such rocks as these.

High Peak (Plate VII), capped by the infertile "Plateau deposits" mentioned above and crowned with an ancient camp, is the outstanding feature of the coast line, for beyond it the red sandstone cliffs are lower where they sweep round to Otterton Point. The mouth of the River Otter, not seen in the picture but easily found on the map, is a good example of the eastward drift of beach materials. The River Sid, reaching the coast at Sidmouth, is almost blocked in the same way. Such drifting has to be taken into account in studying the sites of many a small port. There is evidence of landslip on the east of Map 5, where the arrangement of porous rocks above comparatively impervious strata would tend to cause landslip after a wet season, but this is not visible in Plate V. Examples of invisibility or "dead ground" can be found by comparing Plate V with Map 5, and can be worked out in any hilly district.

What can we see of man's activities in this district? The photograph shows the greater part of a little town covering a mile-wide flood-plain, and extending inland, although the town east of the stream and of the river mouth is hidden by the end of a flat-topped ridge, about 550 feet high, in the foreground of the picture and the east of the map. Most of the buildings are not much above sea-level but some houses of considerable size, with good gardens, straggle up the hillsides. The site of the town still fits into its physical background and is obviously a suitable holiday resort with fine scenery, and sheltered from the north, east and west. No pier, jetty, harbour or lighthouse is seen, and submarine contours do not indicate deep water, so a first glance at the map suggests that this coast bounds a district of mainly agricultural interests, with villages and farms on the lower slopes of the hills. There is no coastal road—the topography is too complicated and perhaps too prone to land-slips, although the cut-off valley of the Sid gives opportunity for a flat "Promenade."

Most coastal settlements began and developed as fishing or commercial ports and were from the first largely influenced by their setting. As a route-junction (between sea and land) they could not grow to any extent without communications inland as well as a convenient approach from the sea. Therefore in early days an inlet, sheltered from wind and sea, was needed.

Formerly fishing, carried on by small boats, was centred on such little natural harbours, often at or near a river-mouth and usually enclosed by a stone pier. Many such are to be found in Cornwall, Yorkshire and elsewhere. As boats became larger, went farther afield, and the fishing industry became more centralized, these little ports declined in commercial import-ance, but, often being situated in attractive surroundings, became resorts for those who wanted quiet holidays, until brought to the notice of motorists. Then their character changed. The history of many holiday resorts may be indicated by the architecture of the period when seaside holidays became popular, and their growth can be traced by distinguishing buildings of this time from older ones, and mapping them accordingly. Later developments, due to improved communica-tions inland and new ideas of amusement, can often be seen, too.

Many ports have grown into large centres of population owing to different reasons—such as nearness or convenient access to fishing grounds, deep water near the coast, facilities for shipbuilding and repairs, or good communications inland or with the continent. A position on an estuary, where produce from the sea or foreign lands can be carried some distance inland before unloading, is favourable and too obvious to need further illustration here; the reader will know of many examples of these, as well as of seaports with long histories which have been superseded by others that could provide for larger boats.

Many estuaries have been artificially deepened and if the district to be studied includes one of these, the soundings and extent and depth of water at high and low tide respectively should be noted. So, too, should the character of the river mouth, whether it narrows or widens downstream, and how far this is due to problems of physical geography.

Many who are interested in natural history will find scope in observing the actual fish brought in and finding out something of their habits, migrations and food, also the conditions under which they are caught. And the wild life of any shoreline, shell fish, sea-weeds and so forth, appeals to some students and would find a place in any coastal survey. Obviously there would be different discoveries on coasts in Plates V, VI and X.

The scene in Plate XII (page 51) is very different from the coasts already considered. The cliffs are of chalk. The photograph suggests at once that the port has other activities than fishing or the amusement of tourists, although these are also to be found there. The town is not on a natural harbour in the ordinary sense of the term; there is no deep, wide estuary, and the sea is not deep, in fact submarine contours widen out in front of the mouth of the valley, and the local physical features form obstacles to the approaches from inland. But the history of the port is very old. There was a Roman port, now silted up, which was lighted by a lighthouse on either side of the inlet where now a town straggles north-westwards up a deep valley which still defines its shape. On Map 6 ($2\frac{1}{2}$ in. to a mile) a little stream is intermittently hidden by buildings, but enough is seen of the physical features to realize the difficulty of approach overland to the port from either east or west. The railways are obliged to use tunnels before reaching the port. Steep high cliffs border the sea and are crowned east of the town by a Norman castle built on the site of a Roman fort. The growth of the port, enlarged as it is by the artificial breakwaters shown in Map 6, and partly shown in Plate XII, is mainly due to its position in that part of the coast which most nearly approaches the continent of Europe, actually within sight of the white cliffs of France, and the importance of this position is shown by the way in which natural obstacles to communications have been overcome.

A local survey in such a centre would include inquiry into the activities of cross-Channel packet boats, the uses made of the port by the Royal Navy, the extent of the fishing industry here, and such trade as may be carried on from that port. Inquiry, however, in any seaport should begin with the observations of the ships themselves, at first-hand. Observations of tides and weather are relevant, too. Information as to the spread of the town up the valley here, compared with the area covered at different periods of its history, might be obtained from old maps and compared with the present-day Ordnance map; the growth of this or of any seaport town should be thought of in connexion with the surrounding physical features, possible communications and the changing activities and interests of the port. Contemporary changes which can actually be watched will suggest other topics of interest as the work goes on.

SOME PROBLEMS AND EXPERIMENTS

(Questions 1, 2, 3, and 6 are the most suitable for beginners and younger students)

1. Find out from a local map or an atlas the distance of your home or school from the sea at its nearest point. Work out how long it would take you to reach the coast either on foot, or by cycle or train, and draw a map of your route.

2. Describe the appearance of the coast in your survey area, and the rocks exposed near the sea. To what geological period do they belong?

3. Notice the beach materials, whether sand, rock, or shingle, and try to find out their origin. Is there any evidence of long-shore drift?

4. Describe and map any sea-caves, sand-dunes, or landslips in the district, and try to account for their presence.

5. Is any sea-fishing carried on in your district? What fish are caught and where are they sent? Has the industry increased or decreased in recent years? Mark on your local map where the fishermen live and where the boats come in.

6. Make sketches, and learn the names of the chief types of ships or boats which come into port in or near your survey area. For what are they used, where do they go, and what cargoes do they carry?

7. If you live near a port on a river estuary, note the range of high and low tide; mark on a map the lowest river crossing and the roads leading to it.

8. If you live in or near a coastal town, find out whether it has grown from a village into either a seaport or pleasure resort, or both. Map those parts of the town which show the changes in its history.

CHAPTER VIII

LOCAL SURVEYS IN URBAN AREAS

IN the districts already studied, we have found much of interest that we can see with our own eyes, and which might lead to a search for more information, but there may be a tendency in studying an urban area, even more than in a rural one, to rely on written records, statistics and inquiries from others. It should therefore be emphasized, again, that personal observation should always be the starting-point, even from such an unpromising view as that in Plate VIII (page 43), and that when the first view and all that it shows is familiar, further inquiries could be made. It has been found that scholars soon begin "to realize that first-hand experience was not everything" and "that as the town came alive to them they wanted to know more of its history and that of the country" and that "one reference led to another and they began to realize how books should really be used."* But surely the town *must* "come alive" by first-hand discovery before the second stage can mean much, and even large-scale maps of closely built-up areas can be very dull until special features, which have been seen, are marked on them.

Factory Chimneys

In Plate VIII the outstanding features are tall factory chimneys. These suggest a visit to a factory if it can be arranged, to see as many processes of the work as possible. Then may follow some research into the sources of raw materials and power used in the factory and the destinations of the finished articles, perhaps linking up with school-work in general geography. Questions of transport will also arise, and this might, to some extent, be watched. It is worth while to find out, too, whether the industry in question is a traditional one in the district or has been recently introduced, and in the former case whether there are any relics of it under early conditions, such as

* *Local Studies*, Ministry of Education pamphlet No. 10, H.M. Stationery Office, 1948.

disused mills or quarries or (possibly) pack-horse lanes leading to it.

But even before, or during, such studies of industry, observation and initiative can be used in noting the heights of the chimneys in relation to the neighbouring houses, and if surveying is taught these can be estimated with a clinometer. Also records could be made of the directions of the wind as shown by the smoke from day to day, followed by noting which parts of the town are the cleanest, and, if it is assumed that in Plate VIII the wind is blowing from the most frequent quarter, shadows should show what time in the day the photograph was taken. Another conspicuous feature is the gasometer, and when its site has been located on the map, inquiries might be made to find out the area served by it, and to what extent gas and electricity are used for domestic and industrial purposes.

Plate VIII shows other buildings. Do they indicate an important period in the growth or history of the town? Their design suggests the nineteenth century. Of what do they appear to be built? Contrast these with the older houses built of local materials in Plate III. The mill in Plate VIII should be observed carefully and its appearance compared with any remains or pictures of older mills, perhaps built of different materials, or with more modern factories. The cottages, too, look grim in comparison with many of later date such as those in Plate X and are without the gardens so characteristic of English homes, but there is an open space (possibly due to enemy action) in the foreground of the picture where rough grass and perhaps some flowering plants (which may be considered "weeds") may be found. These may be identified, listed and studied in relation to the local climate, smoky atmosphere and depth and character of the soil exposed to view here.

Plate VIII shows a scene where nothing seems to be happening at the moment—although it is a built-up area no people are seen—presumably they are all at work indoors. This again may lead to inquiry into hours and conditions of work, but this should be first suggested by a preliminary view, and inquiries should be made with great tact.

If the survey student wandered beyond this immediate

viewpoint probably he would make fresh discoveries. He might find a busier area where traffic is important and this may lead to some of the lines of study discussed in Chapter VI. Nearly every town, too, contains an area where there are either some relics of an interesting past, or pleasing modern buildings, or both. The former will be discussed in the next chapter.

Spread of Suburbs

The size of the built-up area and the spread of a suburb can best be realized by walking or driving slowly through it, referring constantly to a map. The distance covered could then be compared with the area of other towns known to the student and found on other maps of the same scale, and the growth of the town can be realized when compared with its extent on maps of different periods.

We must also think of the town as part of a larger area, and of its geographical setting, rather as we tried to do in the case of a country village. The urban area may be more complicated, and it has been pointed out that a *town plan* may be older than any existing building within it. To find a reason for the site of an existing settlement, maps of a large area are important, especially of physical features which may have influenced communications at different periods, perhaps leading to a market. Therefore the old market-place, or its site, should be located. The question may be considered as to how far the best shops are from it or whether the chief shopping centre has moved away.

The Parish

The position of the parish church and whether the building is old or has been rebuilt or restored is an important question. It may suggest that the parish (whether in town or country) is a good unit for study. There is much of interest in tracing parish boundaries, and as they are marked on the 6 in. and $2\frac{1}{2}$ in. maps, they can be easily followed in the field. It may be found that this boundary depends on physical features which were once considered more important than they are now. If the boundary follows the course of a road or footpath, that route is likely to be of some considerable age.

Architecture

Note the chief features of buildings, whether old or new, industrial or domestic, rich or poor. Roofs, chimneys, doors and windows, each may have some point of interest that throws light on local history and the past character of the country. Even in big cities isolated houses possessing features of great architectural interest may be found hidden away among modern buildings. Are these relics of the original centre, or of formerly detached villages absorbed into the town? These two types are still to be found in the country of Map 1, the stone architecture on the limestone uplands, and the brick, timber and straw, on the clay lowlands to the north and east. Old flint buildings may be expected in chalk country such as that in Plate XI, but all these characteristic styles are rapidly being superseded or hidden by recent buildings. Old buildings give much scope to those who can draw or take photographs.

Street Names

During a walk through the town it is worth while to take note of names of streets, inns and other buildings. These names may refer to Royalties, or other celebrities or men of note in the district, or events in history, or past and present activities of the people, often connected with farming. Readers will at once think of such names as Regent Street, Victoria Street, Trafalgar Square, Waterloo Station, as well as place names that recall the Jubilee of Queen Victoria. Sheep Street, Cornmarket, Green Lane (in London!) and others suggest great changes, and so do such names of inns and hotels as "The Fleece" and "The Hop-Pole," which give some clue to the dates of their origins when such industries were important. But some hotel and street names may have been recently changed and should be checked.

Old Town Maps and Plans

In many towns the Public Library, Museum, or Town Hall possesses maps showing the most important roads at different periods which may have been changed as methods of transport changed. Little narrow alleys between buildings may survive as rights of way, pointing out where more important routes once ran through the town, and these might well be mapped and connected up with communications outside the town. It is a good exercise for beginners to mark and name on a large-scale map any new buildings not shown on the published copy, recognized road crossings, bus stops, or "islands" personally known to the scholars. Children also might well practise estimating distances, and the gradients of roads within the town. The physical foundation of a town-site "comes alive" most effectively if contours are traced from the 6 in. map and the spaces between them coloured or shaded according to altitude. It is good experience, too, for children to practise describing a route clearly and accurately from one point to another.

Local Water Supply

This is, of course, immensely important, and often leads back to problems of physical geography and geology. Sources of a town's water, in past and present, might be compared. The reservoir where water is now stored should be visited if it is not too far away; the geographical setting of artificial or partly artificial lakes which supply the towns are very often enlightening as well as beautiful. They illustrate, too, some of the ways in which town and country are bound together by important interests.

Sources of water supply differ much under modern conditions and inquiry is necessary in urban areas, but it is all to the good if children (and adults too) can *see* for themselves the spring or lake in hill country from which the water comes. See Map 4 (facing page 30) for an example of springs in a rural area.

It will by this time be realized that the aim of this book is to stress the importance and advantages in local studies of first-hand observation, *before* employment of the many methods of using statistics and descriptive books on the district and making charts and diagrams from them. It is not, however, suggested that these, important and enlightening as they are, should be neglected. Information about such methods, often particularly telling in Social Studies, can be gained from books more directly concerned with the study of Citizenship. There is not space to enlarge on them here, but as a local survey progresses it will be evident that an approach through personal observation can well be made even to those studies which must, eventually, be mainly worked out "on paper."

A Seaport

In addition to the problems mentioned above, others may arise in the commercial study of a seaport town as that in Map 6, and Plate XII (already dealt with in Chapter VII), and here observation should take a prominent place. The study might begin *either* with the consideration of the town-site and neighbouring coast, *or* with its commercial activities, which perhaps can be observed more easily in a seaport than in an inland town. For there is much to be learned from watching ships.

Past and Future

To many, the future is more fascinating than the past, and any schemes for future planning (such as uses to be made of open spaces, or new building sites) may well be discussed from various points of view. But young people should surely be encouraged to realize that, for the most part, present conditions are developments of the past. Therefore, as no local survey is complete without reference to the past history of the district, this aspect of the subject will be considered next.

SOME PROBLEMS AND EXPERIMENTS

(Questions 4, 5, 6, 7, 11, and 12 are the most suitable for beginners and younger students)

1. Compare in size the built-up areas in Maps 2 and 4 with those on the map of your nearest village or town. Try to find from your local map the extent of the spread of building since the publication of the map and add this information to it.

2. Look carefully at the site of your parish church and manor house (if any), and mark them on a physical map showing contours and water only. Do you think that the settlement developed from this point?

3. Is your market held out of doors or in a covered hall? If the latter, find the site of the old market-place. How far is the present market from the chief shopping centre to-day? Look at the cattle market (if any) and draw a sketch map of the roads leading to it.

4. On your local map measure distances from school to (a) your home, (b) the church, (c) the post office, (d) the hospital, (e) the cinema, (f) the railway station, (g) nearest bridge over a river. How long does it take you to walk to these places, and how would you direct a visitor, arriving at the station, to any of them?

5. Look carefully at any factory chimneys near by. What is their height relatively to the surrounding houses? Which way does the smoke usually blow? Mark on the map any new factories which have been built since its publication.

6. What signs of the industry carried on in these factories can you *see*?

7. Make lists of names of (*a*) any streets, (*b*) any public-houses which refer to past industries or country life, and mark these on a map.

8. Which is the most crowded traffic-centre in your town? What improvements would you suggest? Draw a sketch map of roads used by motor buses.

9. Note the position of the railway station. Is it in the town or outside it? Has the old town grown towards it? Where is the nearest tunnel?

10. If you are near the sea, map all streets leading to the pier or quay. Try to find out what cargoes arrive, or the kinds of fish caught, and their seasons.

11. List the wild flowers which you find growing in your district in empty spaces (perhaps due to bombing) or on railway embankments.

12. Make a list, and either draw or photograph the birds you can feed in winter. Where do they come from?

CHAPTER IX

APPROACH TO LOCAL SURVEYS THROUGH HISTORY

SUCH an approach might be chosen under certain circumstances —for instance if history were the chief interest of the leader of the group or some prominent members of it, and if the region offered scope for their hobbies and experience. Or, there might be one or more outstanding buildings or sites, or even traditions, so important in the locality that the survey could start with them, and sooner or later branch out into other local interests. A true local survey cannot be limited to records of what happened in the past, though these should be carefully studied in connexion with observational work of present conditions. There is a danger of too much reliance on reading when making a historical study. Therefore in this approach, just as much as in others, accurate observation and skilled map-reading are needed.

A Preliminary Exploration of Historic Sites

As an example, let us see how a survey can be approached in this way, in the area covered by Map 2, ignoring all that we have already studied there. In a preliminary exploration, preferably on foot, we may choose to walk along the summit of the escarpment, to get a wide view at once. On the way we shall find earthworks on Painswick Hill (which can be seen in the south of Map 2 and in the centre of the skyline in Plate II), and on Brotheridge indicated on the left of Plate I, and on Crickley Hill on the east of Map 2. On the map these are marked "Camp" in lettering which gives them a pre-Roman date—for they were made by the people of the Early Iron Age, who were here before and during the Roman occupation. Such earthworks are often so fragmentary that it is difficult to reconstruct from our own imagination. Books and drawings by experts sometimes help, and papers about them in scientific journals can sometimes be found in a local library, but, failing such evidence, it is always possible to examine the sites for ourselves, to see how the earthworks could be approached, what could be seen from them, in short, why they were built *just there*. The probable extent and position of former forests (if this can be discovered), the nearest water-supply, the geological foundation, and the height above sea-level are all important, and the uses, if any, to which camps have been put in later times, including possibly the last war, are of interest. The site of a pre-Roman camp in Map 5 can be compared with those already examined.

Having studied the positions of these in the field and on the local map, we might next look for any other objects marked in the same type (of pre-Roman date) and look at the sites or relics of these.

Barrows or Tumuli

In Map 2 we find "West Tump" at a height of about 900 feet, in Cranham woods, and a "Long Barrow" Tumulus high up on Shurdington Hill. Inquiry will tell us that these were long, low mounds, made about 4000 years ago for tombs of the Neolithic (or New Stone Age) chieftains and their families, in which their bones and often their treasured possessions have been found (here a warning may be given that "treasure hunting" or unskilled digging by children or by inexperienced adults, may do irreparable damage to any further scientific research). These barrows are the oldest remains in this as in many other districts, and may lead to study of absorbing interest. It is worth while to look for fragments of flint on high ground near these monuments, and to compare them with the specimens in the nearest museum, where there may also be fragments of the pottery and bones of the animals of that time. The background of physical geography and geology is important. These early people chose dry and usually high ground where movement was easier than in forested clay land, and where the Tumuli would have been conspicuous objects seen from afar. They were obviously much higher, when first built, than they are to-day. In Map 2 other Tumuli are marked in the same type—actually these latter were tombs of the Bronze Age people of a later date, though there was some overlapping. These, known to archaeologists as "Round Barrows," are smaller than the long ones of the New Stone Age and are often so much ploughed over that they are hard to recognize. Though the men who made them knew the use of metal, melting tin and copper to form bronze, they also used flint implements, but their arrow-heads are different and easier to recognize than those of their predecessors. They were good craftsmen and went far afield for the sake of trade in metals. It should be remembered that flint is found naturally only in chalk, therefore when it is found on other geological formations the little implements, or flakes chipped from them, must have been brought there by early peoples. So, in this area, we have already found relics in the field of the peoples of three distinct periods of history—Neolithic from about 2500 B.C., Bronze Age from 1900 B.C. and Early Iron Age from about 500 B.C. onwards. When students have actually seen such relics and studied their sites, any reading on the subject will seem very much more worth while.

It must be confessed, however, that not all districts include relics of these very early times. We do not expect to find them on land which was formerly forested, or where the undrained land was swampy, but there are few districts in England where there are no traces of the Roman occupation.

Roman Sites

Some of the earliest relics of this time are the great military roads which crossed the country in straight lines from one point to another, though not straight throughout their whole course. Many of these roads have been continuously in use until the present day, the foundations of many remain and, even where some have for a long while been disused, the line of route can often be traced by a path or boundary, sometimes continuing the line of an existing road. Part of one of these important and historic roads is shown on Map 2. Here it connects the Roman town of Corinium (now Cirencester, beyond the south-east corner of the map) with the Severn crossing at Glevum (now Gloucester). Note the type of printing used for this road. There must have been, of course, many minor roads and trackways, now lost, which led to sites such as the splendid country houses known as "Villas," the foundations of which are found in many districts of southern England. The site of a fine example is marked on Maps 1 and 2 and can be seen on the lower slopes of the spur opposite the photographer in Plate I. The sites of these large, almost self-supporting estates, occupied either by Roman officials or by "natives" who became rich and prosperous farmers when the country was "settled," are interesting in contrast to those of the pre-Roman camps near by. Villas were usually placed near a good spring, on fertile soil in shelter from storms, and nearly always with a beautiful view! All this may well be studied in the field even where little of the building remains. So, too, should the appearance of the Roman roads as they sweep across the country, often raised up, still, above the land on either side. Many of our cities have Roman foundations, too, and the devastation of the last war has made open spaces where these foundations can be investigated. Much is being discovered, gradually, as to the early history of some of these centres. In the north and west of Britain, where the country was more likely to be disturbed under the Roman occupation, there are naturally fewer of the rich country houses, but remains of Roman fortresses and camps still exist. Local maps will indicate where these are, and a visit to a museum which shows what has been found will help to reconstruct the life of the times, but a study of the *site* makes it much more vivid, and should supplement any historical reading about it, and such observations add interest to any Roman coins which may be dug up in gardens or fields near such a site.

Medieval and Later Buildings

Returning to Maps 1 and 2, yet another style of printing is seen; for example, a Moat in the north-east of Map 2 and Tocknells Court, a fine seventeenth-century house in the south of it. To the west of Cranham is Prinknash Park, with a house dating from Tudor times (now a monastery), also printed in this way, which refers to buildings of historic interest *later* than those of the Roman occupation. If names, printed thus, are seen on your local maps, the sites should be visited to see how much remains and to what use, if any, the building is now put; the choice of these sites, notably in the case of monastic buildings, must have had some reason which can be worked out. Medieval castles would also be shown in this way and would be exciting centres from which a survey could expand. The materials of which these old buildings are constructed can be related to local geology. Architecture is a clue to the age of post-Roman buildings and is a study in itself, but again the origin of the building materials used, as well as the other requirements (such as water supply) of any ancient site, lead back to those problems of physical geography and geology which are always present.

Parish Churches

Many villages, in all parts of the country, have something of historic interest in their parish churches, which were built of more durable materials than the smaller houses of the time, and are often all that remains of the past. Details in churches, such as windows, tombs, screens, brasses, are admired and could be sketched. Less often are they thought of in connexion with the life of the period, although tombs and "brasses" may show us the contemporary costumes as well as the individual skill of the craftsmen. Parish records, if available, shed some light on the past life of the district, but these records are more vivid if the setting is understood. Old maps can sometimes be consulted, but even without them something may be done by tracing from modern 6 in. maps the physical features of the district, adding only those buildings which probably existed in the period of study.

Sites of Historic Buildings

If there is but one building of outstanding historical interest in or near your town or village, it might be well to concentrate on this—the materials of which it is built and their sources, the probable conditions of the surrounding country and what can be discovered about the lives of the people of the time. In the case of a city which contains many relics of the past it might be well to begin by attempting a study of the city at the time of its greatest importance, mapping all the relics that remain from that period, and noting those that can be seen in local museums. Old records and maps preserved in the town may help to reconstruct the life of the time and contrasts should be noted between that period and the conditions in the same town to-day.

If any relics of town walls exist they are, like castles, vivid reminders of the different outlook in the past. These often show fortifications of different periods. The coaching inns of a later time need to be studied as part of a wide area, their sites having close connexion with communications which existed when they were important. The site of the castle in Plate XI and the earthworks in Plate XII should be studied in connexion with Map 6 or, if possible, with a map of a larger area. Some districts include the site of a battle, which may be meaningless to students unless the larger movements of the campaign are worked out and mapped on a small-scale physical map.

Markets, Fairs and Local Traditions

Markets were referred to in Chapter V. Some of them have very long histories, suggested by the interesting and often very beautiful market-halls to be found in many country towns. Also referred to in Chapter V are the fairs for special commodities and also for amusements, held annually in many old towns, and sometimes connected originally with church festivals. Old inhabitants of the district may be able to tell of many changes in these fairs during their lifetime. The original purpose of the fair, the people who benefited by it, and the routes by which the produce was brought to it, are full of interest. So, too, are legends and tales of the district, and stories of old customs such as May Day festivals and Mumming plays, and old songs, and crafts, but care should be taken to distinguish those with a long tradition from modern revivals such as some of the folk-dancing now so popular. Old inhabitants may also be able to tell us the field names, and the paths and rights of way now in danger of being lost.

The Study of Architecture

There is, of course, immense scope for the study of the past in our cathedrals and many abbey churches, especially where the architecture has developed over a long period, and there have been additions or re-building. Special architectural style is often connected with the resources of the district, or with the activities of the time, as in the case of the glorious Perpendicular churches built during and as a result of the wealth of the great days of England's wool trade—churches in which can be seen the tombs and "brasses" of the merchants who helped to build them, and from which much may be learned about the dress of the period. Some Georgian and Regency architecture dates from the time when visits to "spas" or to the seaside first became fashionable, and the Industrial Revolution had an unhappy effect on the spread of ugliness in many towns (Plate VIII), while blocked-up windows give evidence of a former window-tax. These developments too should be considered in connexion with the coming of the railways and the growth of towns towards them, referred to in Chapter VI, and all this can be linked on to lessons both in English history and in physical and economic geography. Even a slight knowledge of architectural styles in the home town adds interest to a holiday elsewhere, when other styles can be compared with them. But the fact must be faced that every year such distinctions are being obliterated by the spread of new buildings which have no connexion with local materials. So the direct influence of the geographical background is also becoming less obvious. Even now, however, it is worth while to trace from a 6 in. or $2\frac{1}{2}$ in. map the physical setting of a town, bearing in mind that even this may have changed during historic times—the sea may have encroached on the land, or the land on the sea, or the mouth of a river may have become silted up (Map 5) or an artificial lake made (Map 2), while forests may have been felled, and swamps drained. This may involve some study of old maps, which should be carefully compared with those of to-day.

We will end with the thought that just as we occupy a definite place in the world and so are living in "geography," we are also living in "history" and the two so-called "subjects" cannot be separated. Even some of our ancient monuments have had their recent uses, and many are still used. Services have been held without a break from Norman times, and sometimes earlier, in many cathedrals and parish churches. The Iron Age camp in Plate II and Map 2 was used by the Home Guard in the late war; the castle in Plate XI is still occupied; some country houses have been in the same family for generations. Moreover many customs and activities which seem ordinary and everyday happenings to us, and many innovations now being made, will, in course of time, be of historical interest and therefore should be watched and recorded in any thorough and careful study of even a small district.

SOME PROBLEMS AND EXPERIMENTS

(Questions 1, 2, 5, 6, and 7 are the most suitable for beginners and younger students)

1. What are the sites or buildings in your district that are most visited by tourists, and why do they visit them? What could you tell a visitor about one of these places?

2. Try to find the oldest building in your survey area. Is it in ruins or still in use? What use was made of it in the past, and for what is it now used?

3. If you live near a Long Barrow (Neolithic) or a Round Barrow (Bronze Age), draw a picture of it and a sketch map of the surrounding country. Write notes on the people who made it.

4. If you live near an Iron Age or a Roman camp, make a plan of the earthworks that remain, and find and mark the nearest spring. Make a sketch map of the roads leading to it, and describe what can be seen from it.

5. Describe some objects in the nearest museum which were found in your district, and draw sketch maps to show where they were found.

6. Make a list of the houses in your town or village which have dates on the outside, and mark them on the 6-in. map. Of what are these houses built?

7. Make a list of the names of lanes and roads near you which refer to some event in history. What do these tell you of their dates?

8. If you are near a coaching inn, find out the destinations to which the coaches ran, and make a map of the roads they used. Map any toll-houses that they would have passed.

9. What industries were carried on in your survey area long ago? Do any of these survive? How have conditions changed (a) in methods of work, (b) in the lives of the workers?

10. If any local legends refer to any special place in your survey area, describe and, if possible, photograph it as it is to-day.

11. Describe in detail any architecture which seems to you to throw light on the history of your parish church.

INDEX